To Christen Jedlicki

Neil F. Pierre

The Sun and the Umbrella

The Sun
and the Umbrella

NELS F. S. FERRÉ

PROFESSOR OF PHILOSOPHICAL THEOLOGY
VANDERBILT UNIVERSITY SCHOOL OF RELIGION

Harper & Brothers . Publishers
New York

TO

RICHARD M. VAUGHAN

CHRISTIAN SCHOLAR

AND

LARGE-HEARTED FRIEND

Contents

7

Preface

Someone is sure to say: "An umbrella is for rain; he means 'sunshade.'" Let such a person look up the root meaning of the word "shade"!

No parable walks on all fours. Neither does the book. Its purpose is, like that of the parable, to make emphatic one point: the Gospel is the good news of God. Whatever hinders the news is bad; whatever helps is good. For instance, we pray "*through* Christ our Lord." He is Lord of our lives only if we do get *through* to God.

One night in Zürich Emil Brunner read the parable. His first reaction was that it was a new version of Luther's *Commentary on Galatians*. The point is that we must do what Peter Forsyth asked of us: to continue and carry through the Reformation. Charles Clayton Morrison calls the task "The Unfinished Reformation." Many will be shocked by what I say, but I believe that many more will find God real. When He becomes real, life finds joyful purpose and creative drive.

The substance of these chapters was given at the Candler School of Theology, Emory University, as the Jones Lectures. My thanks to its faculty, students, alumni and friends for their vigorous response. I am also thankful for generous help from my wife, the editorial department of Harper & Brothers, and Miss Lorine Martin, who typed the manuscript.

The inspiration of the parable came like lightning early one morning as I was praying about our secondhand religious experience. After that came the hard work. The result is for the reader to judge. In any case, I leave the book with confidence in the hands of God.

The Sun
and the Umbrella

The Sun and the Umbrella

Once upon a time there were some people who lived under an Umbrella. The amusing thing about them was that they called themselves SUNWORSHIPERS. They had not always lived there. Their former domicile was the House of Legality. This was an old barn, very wide but of low ceiling, and with no windows in it. The Lamps of the Law kept the people busy lighting them, for they smoked and went out easily. Therefore the light in the old barn was very dim. And so the people sighed, waiting for new and brighter Light to appear, but while century after century went by the people went to their graves in disappointment.

Then one day came a prophet with a new light on his face. He told them there was bright sunshine outside. All they needed to do to test his truth was to step out and see for themselves. But they feared to do so. He said: "I come from the Light; I know the Light. I am of the Light. Trust me. Follow me into the Light." Many listened. Many marveled. But as he kept pleading with them to leave the dark barn for the light of the Sun, they became angry and hated him. They

13

said he spoke ill of their great dwelling place, reared at untold expense by their former prophets and forefathers. After all, how could anyone now living know more about the Light than did the wisest scholars and noblest prophets of old? The more they thought on this obvious truth, the more they resented his claim. Finally they decided to kill this impostor, who, after all, would only lead their young ones away from the Light secured for them at so great cost. And they killed him.

But some among them had trusted the young prophet and some had even ventured out into the sunshine with him to find it real. They had not gone very far, to be sure, because the bright sunshine had hurt their eyes, unused to it as they were. They had kept themselves mostly inside the House of Legality. When the prophet was dead, however, they could not deny that there actually was sunshine outside and that the sunshine was a stronger Light than even that of the Lamps of the Law. As they then studied the writings about the Light to come which were written by their own prophets, they became convinced that the young prophet was the bringer of that Light and they worshiped him as their Lord and Leader. He had delivered them from darkness and made a way for them into the Light. Yet they could now neither be happy inside the House nor dared they yet go out into the strong Sun. Therefore they built themselves an Umbrella, large and strong, under which they all walked out into the Sun. Inside the Umbrella they wrote: "We are the SUNWORSHIPERS. We believe in him who said that we ought to leave the House of Legality to live in the Sun. All who want to live in the Sun must now come under our Umbrella. Leave the dark House of Legality, even with its Lamps of the Law, and dare to venture out into the Sun under our Umbrella." And many did.

Soon, however, wise men among them said: "We may shortly forget what our Prophet told us about the Sun and how to live in its light. He alone comes from the Sunshine and knows about it. Let us therefore now make for ourselves writings which shall preserve for us and for our children the truths about the Sun." Thereupon they built themselves another Umbrella under the Large One, inside which they recorded the holy testimony of those who themselves knew the Prophet who alone knew the Sun. The holy words recorded, as carefully as possible, what the first followers into the Sun knew about the Prophet, what He had told them about the Sun, and how all who followed Him should live unafraid in its light.

But even their wisest men disputed among themselves concerning what the words which were written inside the new Umbrella meant and who had the right to interpret them, whereupon they set about gradually to construct a third Umbrella, inside the second, which they called the Church. On the under side of this new Umbrella they wrote: "Gather here all who want to accept the Prophet who came from the Sun and taught us to live in the Sun. We are the true SUNWORSHIPERS. Outside this Umbrella no one can be sure of the Sun, nor that it truly lights, warms and heals us. We know only Him and what the writings tell of Him as these are authoritatively interpreted for us by those under this Umbrella called the Church. Come under this Umbrella all ye who want to live in the light of the Sun. We are the true SUNWORSHIPERS."

Nevertheless fear arose. Some did not trust even the teachings of the savants under the Church. Even the large Umbrella plus both the others could not make them feel secure about the Sun. They said: "Let us now interpret the writings

for ourselves to arrive at the original words of our Lord and
Leader. Let us accept Him only and what He did for us and
taught us." Some of these made themselves smaller Umbrellas
inside which they wrote formulas, called creeds, concerning
that which was really important in the original writings and
kept repeating these formulas about the Prophet who came
from the Sun and told them to come out to live in the light
of the Sun. Others picked out this saying or that for their
little Umbrellas as the most important clue to understanding
and the most obedient way of accepting the Prophet and His
message concerning their living in the Sun.

It happened, however, that one of their number began to
wonder about the Umbrellas. He read over and over again the
words of the Prophet to the effect that they should LIVE in
the Sun; that to honor him was to follow him into the sunshine. And so he went forth into the sunshine. At first, to be
sure, the Light hurt his eyes and for a while he longed to
return under the Umbrellas. As he grew used to living in the
light of day, however, he grew happier and happier about it.
At last he could no longer bear not to tell his friends under
the Umbrellas about his new life in the Sun. He returned
with great joy to let his friends know that the Prophet was
right. Not only could they leave the dark, old barn with the
Lamps of the Law, but they could even leave the Umbrellas—
all of them—to live in the Sunlight itself!

They looked at him with mingled feelings of hope and fear,
of temptation and resistance, of near-belief and hurt. At last
they cried out, however, "You dishonor our Prophet! You
scorn our Umbrellas! Apart from him and apart from these
we know no Sun, whether it can help us and whether we can
live in its light." The young man who had himself tried the

words of the Prophet and who knew for himself that in the Light was the best place to live tried to tell his friends that in order to honor the Prophet they must not merely call him their Lord and Leader but take him at his word and move out into the Sunlight. And some listened and came out, at first with pain but then with unbelievable joy; and they would not again return under the Umbrellas to find the Sun. But others preferred the way of faith in the Umbrellas and heeded not his word. Instead they went on praising the Prophet of the Sun while living under the Umbrellas. "After all," they said, "we know that we have been freed from the darkness of the House of Legality." And they went on so believing.

Those who now were in the Light, however, could not forbear to go everywhere to tell about that Light. Not only did they return to those who worshiped the Sun under the Umbrellas while averring to live fully in its Light, but they also went into the House of Legality to share their good news with the people there, and they ventured into all the earth, into Houses of strange religions, and into all Houses where in sundry fashions men tried to find and to live in the Light. As they kept telling the good news of the Light their joy increased, and the time being ready, there was a great and joyful exodus from all Umbrellas and Houses into the Light.

I

An Umbrella Called Christ

Once upon a time there were some people who lived under an Umbrella. The amusing thing about them was that they called themselves SUNWORSHIPERS. They had not always lived there. Their former domicile was the House of Legality. This was an old barn, very wide but of low ceiling, and with no windows in it. The Lamps of the Law kept the people busy lighting them, for they smoked and went out easily. Therefore the light in the old barn was very dim. And so the people sighed, waiting for a new and brighter Light to appear, but while century after century went by the people went to their graves in disappointment.

Then one day came a prophet with a new light on his face. He told them there was bright sunshine outside. All they needed to do to test his truth was to step out and see for themselves. But they feared to do so. He said: "I come from the Light; I know the Light. I am of the Light. Trust me. Follow me into the light." Many listened. Many marveled. But as he kept pleading with them to leave the dark barn for the light of the Sun, they became angry and hated him. They

18

said he spoke ill of their great dwelling place, reared at untold expense by their former prophets and forefathers. After all, how could anyone now living know more about the Light than did the wisest scholars and noblest prophets of old? The more they thought on this obvious truth, the more they resented his claim. Finally they decided to kill this impostor, who, after all, would only lead their young ones away from the Light secured for them at so great cost. And they killed him.

But some among them had trusted the young prophet and some had even ventured out into the sunshine with him to find it real. They had not gone very far, to be sure, because the bright sunshine had hurt their eyes, unused to it as they were. They had kept themselves mostly inside the House of Legality. When the prophet was dead, however, they could not deny that there actually was sunshine outside and that the sunshine was a stronger Light than even that of the Lamps of the Law. As they then studied the writings about the Light to come which were written by their own prophets, they became convinced that the young prophet was the bringer of that Light and they worshiped him as their Lord and Leader. He had delivered them from darkness and made a way for them into the Light. Yet they could now neither be happy inside the House nor dared they yet go out into the strong Sun. Therefore they built themselves an Umbrella, large and strong, under which they all walked out into the Sun. Inside the Umbrella they wrote: "We are the SUNWORSHIPERS. We believe in him who said that we ought to leave the House of Legality to live in the Sun. All who want to live in the Sun must now come under our Umbrella. Leave the dark House of Legality, even with its Lamps of the Law, and dare to venture out into the Sun under our Umbrella." And many did.

Most of us have our Umbrellas and live under them, if indeed we have dared to venture at all from our dim Houses. We find it hard to worship God directly. He seems unreal, or, at least, far away and indefinite. So for the most part we worship Him through some human institution or tradition which thereby becomes for us, largely, our effective God. We mean to worship God Himself. We do not intend to worship the merely his- torical or the merely human. We should indeed blush to admit, not only to others, but to ourselves, that we worship the human. But the more-than-human seems less real than the human. So we linger inside a familiar House or at best go outside under cover of an Umbrella in order to worship the Sun!

The Hebrews worshiped God centrally through the Law. God, the ineffably Great, had graciously chosen to reveal His will for them in the *Torah*, their Law or Teachings. Their first duty in worshiping God was to keep the Law. To be sure, the Law was not always merely a matter of doing the will of God. At its best it was, as it still is, a living Way of trusting the loving-kindness of the Lord God to His people. It was, assur- edly, a way of faith and gratitude as well as of obedience. No one can understandingly read and accept the Old Testament or know anything of the Jewish commentary on it through the ages, without realizing that to call the whole religion of Israel the House of Legality is a caricature. Nor can anyone today know Jewish piety at its highest without feeling depth of devotion, faith and gratitude, as well as sacrifice and commu- nity concern—all of which outstrip and transform any legalism. Nevertheless, the heart of the Jewish religion was faith in God through the Law of Moses.

As a prominent European rabbi recently affirmed: "God, out

of His infinite wisdom and goodness, has given the Jewish people a way to walk in, which is not only general, but is made up of concrete duties to Him, to the fellow Jew, and to the Gentile. To be a good Jew means to live by the faith that nothing is known by the Jewish people of God or of His will outside this concrete revelation. Theirs is not to judge what God may reveal or withhold from others, but in thankfulness and in holy obedience to walk in the way of the *Torah*."

Through the centuries there has been, to be sure, a strain of Jewish mysticism, an experience or claim to know God directly, often even to know Him as Love. Certainly the great Prophets knew that God spoke to them directly, leading them by His mighty hand in an immediate, personal manner. As a whole, however, Judaism has never stressed that all should know God directly in the manner of Jeremiah's prophesied New Covenant, where no one shall teach his neighbor or brother to know the Lord, for all shall know Him. The chief claim has been, rather, that Judaism is basically a matter of the faithful walking in the Law of Moses and of the Prophets.

This whole way of life Jesus repudiated. He pitched his life with God against Jewish orthodoxy. Therefore, he had to die. He bade people come out into God's sunshine. This invitation was received as a threat to those whose inner security and effective loyalty were tied to the Law as the way to God. Though the Law was developed as a means to make God real, it became likewise a substitute for Him, to the point that its devotees did not effectively recognize His voice when it came from one who knew Him directly and who lived His fuller will. The good news of the Sun, of God's constant availability to His children, came to that people whose god was the Law as a threat to the very meaning of their lives.

Even those who have high loyalties to God use limited means in the worship of Him. These limited means all too easily become confused and identified with Him. Such confusion permits collective selfishness to become subconsciously camouflaged behind a holy zeal for a limited cause. Within this zeal worshipers feel themselves to be a favorite group over against other peoples. In this general sense Judaism lived, and still largely lives, in the House of Legality. The disclosure of God's fuller will as love—complete concern for each and all everywhere—does to death the Law as the highway to God. The Law is displaced as the primary way of knowing and serving God. The fact that God wants us to know Him, to love Him and to walk with Him in personal communion and community, comes, therefore, not only as good news to those within the House of Legality, but also as a threat to their chief pride and joy. In the clear light of the Sun the substitutes for God are seen for what they are: they take the effective place of God both in the mind and in the affection of the worshiper.

The fact is irrefutable, in any case, that man both means to worship God and tries to shut Him out. We both need God and dread His fuller will for us. While we long for nothing so much as for His love and to live in love with one another, we, at the same time, both lack and dread love. Precisely because we are basically created for love, it demands everything of us. Therefore at least subconsciously, we cry out our sin and beg God not to come too near. God wants more of us than we are willing to give and for that reason, even though we need Him, we try to shut Him out. Hence our Houses and our Umbrellas.

Then one day came a prophet with a new light on his

face. He told them there was bright sunshine outside. All they needed to do to test his truth was to step out and see for themselves.

Inevitably at its heart the Christian faith is the Evangel; it is the Story of the Sun, the Story of God's love for all men. It is the unequivocal affirmation that the sovereign Lord of the Universe is also saving Love. It is the unconditional declaration that whatever happens is in the hands of God and that from His hands we receive nothing but good. Even the lowest depths of degradation, chosen by man, are but shallow self-assertions in comparison with the bottomless mercy and restoring power of God. Nature's rawest edge is but part of the full plan to control our astonishingly large and responsible measure of freedom which has itself been bestowed upon us for the sake of our truest eventual good: a free and loving fellowship with God and with one another. The whole heart of the Christian faith is the endless and the ultimately victorious love of God for which we are made and to which we are called. Nothing higher and nothing better can be imagined; if it could be, that, too, would be part of the central truth of the Christian faith: that the sovereign Lord is saving Love.

Therefore, we can fully trust Him. Therefore, we can fully commit our whole lives to Him. Therefore, we can find within the warmth and strength of His love the warmth and strength of the kind of community for which we are made. We do not first have to be good in order to experience the goodness of God or to be welcomed into His presence. He takes us as we are and makes us good. This is the good news for those who have striven in vain in the way of the Law—a good news backed by the solid experience of those who have given God their lives completely. Only Love can cast out fear; only God can conclusively overcome our otherwise uncontrollable anxiety.

Nor must we prove Him real by thinking before coming to Him. We come to Him, rather, with our problems of thought and He, cleansing our hearts and eyes, gives us light as we need both for the day and for the night. A new kind of light breaks forth with power for those who accept the Gospel of the love of God. Nor do we first have to prove God in terms of the facts of His creation. We come to Him, rather, in terms of simple trust, thereby finding that many facts fall into a new context in terms of which their very meaning is illuminated. They now abet instead of stand in the way of our faith. Instead of dreading intellectual insecurity, we find that God's love in us sharpens our intellectual integrity on experience's emery board of patient trusting. God's love does not eliminate our problems (for if it could do so there would have been no need for our earthly existence in the first place), but it gives us light and power, according to our faith and need, increasingly to overcome the problems which we must face.

The Christian faith is a total Gospel, unconditional good news from God's side. It is up to us to open our eyes, to accept and to live in the Light, to prove for ourselves that God, really and fully, is love. When the full Gospel comes, we need neither House nor Umbrella, except, of course, to protect the hardness of our hearts, the weakness of our faith, and the shortsightedness of our vision. These defects do exist, alas, seemingly almost a part of our human nature; and, therefore, we shall always have "houses," except as the Gospel is understood and accepted. To those who do not know God or trust His power, even the thought of radical change is utopianism. For them to believe in God more than in our actual world is to be naïve. Those who know the power of God, however, radically to change lives and the world know that the Gospel is true. Consequently, they long to free others within its power. *This truth and this concern make up the heart of Christian evangelism.*

Unfortunately, the face of God has been hid under Christian Umbrellas. The power of the Sun seldom falls directly on the worshipers. The healing rays of the Sun are deflected, thrown back and absorbed by the Umbrellas under which the Gospel of God as Love is proclaimed. Even Christian theology can be an effective Umbrella against the full light of the Sun. Much of the formulation of the Christian faith is made out of a closely woven fabric under which alone the early disciples dared to leave the House of Legality. Can we now sift, in some way, what is Light from what is Umbrella? The task has to be done. First let us make a general statement about Jesus and then try to see what theology did with the Gospel figure.

Jesus himself came from the sunlight; he knew it personally and taught it confidently; he lived it thoroughly, died on account of his espousal of it, and lives eternally within its power.

Even though, as general affirmations, the above statements are true, there are many historic problems connected with them. Some competent scholars, like George Foote Moore, for instance, believe that Jesus never broke, at least formally, with the Jewish Law as the way of life. This claim, in one sense, may well be true, but in the deeper sense the new wine of the centrality of the love of God could not be poured into the older Jewish bottles without bursting them. Jesus knew this. Furthermore, it is true that the reinterpretation of the Law in terms of a living Way, similar and close to the thought of Jesus, was carried on by contemporary Jewish rabbis. Jesus was, in one sense, a leading Jewish rabbi and must always be understood as such. When all is said and done, however, our era is not the Common Era, but the era After our Lord. His was a revolutionary understanding and acceptance of the centrality for faith and life of God as Love. Or, it is truer to say, in him God who is Love thrust Himself radically into and athwart human history. Jesus' human acceptance of God is far secondary to God's own preparation and initiative in coming into history through him.

Another problem connected with these central affirmations as stated above is the extent to which Jesus himself saw this Gospel and carried it through into systematic form. Some thinkers even question whether he fully enacted it in his own life. Did he completely teach and live God's love? Honesty demands humility of knowledge at this point.

We have no original writings of Jesus but only composite reports concerning his work and words, recorded later by different writers. The writings differ enough, too, to indicate that it is impossible to distinguish, definitely and accurately, between the original figure of Jesus and interpretations of him. Nor can we tell unerringly what is fact and what is fiction, what is reporting and what is veneration. The disciples are often reported to have misunderstood their Master, and certainly the Gospel writers mixed their own thinking and attitudes into what they reported at second hand. Even so, the New Testament as a whole radiates the love of God with a brilliance which cannot be explained apart from the Original Son of God's love. There is no question what constitutes the living heart of the Gospel. It is a new understanding of God as a total stance or context. This God is the key truth to everything constructive in the New Testament. This God is the master key to all intellectual problems concerning ultimate truth and man's nature and destiny.

It is altogether probable, therefore, that this radically new revelation came through one who knew God to be love, who at least saw many major implications of this truth, and whose life can be explained basically only in its terms. The life of Jesus, from the Temptation through Gethsemane and the Cross, speaks experientially with too authentic a voice to be denied: although the fact cannot, by the nature of the case, be demonstrated beyond all doubt, there is firm historic ground to believe that Jesus knew God directly to be radical Love, that he understood himself to be Son of this Love, and that he assumed himself, at the same time, to be a fully normal human being.

What, however, has theology done through the centuries with this Gospel and with this figure? How was the life of Jesus mythologized even in the New Testament? First, the writers could not quite deny tensions, fear and problems in the life of Jesus, but it did present him as sinless, and thereby robbed him of his humanity. All men have sinned and come short of the glory of God. Our solidarity as men in our present existence is, for one part, based on our community in sin. Our deepest problem as men is not finiteness, but sin; not law, but sin; not death, but sin. The Christian faith believes not that God is too holy to behold sin but that He comes to seek and to save the sinner. The Christian faith knows no absolute, either, which like an inverted rainbow dips from the eternal into finite existence only to return again to perfection; God Himself, in coming to save us, rather, for our sake "becomes sin"; He lives with us, among us, in us and for us.

Jesus himself recognized this: He was baptized by John unto the remission of sin to fulfill all righteousness. When someone called him good, he refused the title in deep humility ascribing goodness to God alone. The prayer which he shared with his disciples acknowledged the need for forgiveness. In Gethsemane he cried in agony: 'Not my will, but thine." The other writers, with insight, realized that the sinless had to become sin within full humanity and that Jesus must learn obedience through what he suffered in order to be made perfect. Perfect love casts out fear and whatsoever is not of faith is sin, but Jesus, it was reported, cried day and night out of fear to Him who was able to save him from death. Certainly Jesus was a fully normal human being in all things like ourselves.

But see how theology which does not see, or refuses to see, the full length and depth of the Incarnation distorts the picture and discards the entirety of the Incarnation! By utilizing a few phrases in the New Testament, theology could claim Jesus to be sinless and thus effectively remove him from human nature where he is most needed. If anyone could remain sinless all his life, whatever be his union with God, with no need to know actual alienation from God for the sake of freedom and personal maturity, then our earthly existence is unnecessary. If such a life history were possible with any one man, then God could have made and preserved us all that way from the beginning. Then, indeed, Pelagius was right in teaching that man could remain sinless from birth. Then Jesus, to speak symbolically, came to Paradise and not to Palestine, to the Garden of Eden and not to the sons of Adam. Nor, if Jesus did not share our whole human nature, was there any real victory over sin; for to be human means actually at some time to be over against God through self-will. The idea that anyone could be born into a social environment like ours and yet not participate in our normally natural responses certainly tends to make the savior into a myth. Our solidarity in sin needs to be broken through by our solidarity in grace; our oneness in guilt, by our oneness in God.

Such a view of Jesus as sinless needs a biological Virgin Birth to bolster the miracle. When it is then remembered that raw human nature came also through Mary, what is more natural than to add faith in the Immaculate Conception of Mary? Her Assumption is then, of course, only a short logical step. Finally, Jesus is left as a quasi-human being arbitrarily thrust into history, a stranger to our real nature and burdens, who performs an externally miraculous work, instead of one who, fully human like us, so totally and continuously opened himself to God as Love that he was kept victorious by His power through and beyond a cruel death at the hands of those who hated him.

The fact that the love of God could so invade and so pervade an ordinary human being that through him God became conclusively known and effective in human life is history's greatest miracle. The very changing of our calendar witnesses to this fact. His life is the solid hope for every human being, because it showed that we can likewise receive the love of God and can triumph unto death, and beyond, over the power of sin. Theology hid the real power of Incarnation when it raised the Umbrella of idolatry! The heart of the Christian faith, to repeat, assumes and involves the fact that a sinless God "becomes sin" for our sake, not that He sins but that He cohabits a sinful nature, cleansing it, empowering it and making it new. Therefore, Christ in us is the hope of glory and we can all thereby be given the power to become sons of God.

The reason for stressing this fact of Jesus' full humanity is not a desire to attribute sin to the strong Son of God. His life, in all its crises, was wondrously victorious over temptation. We all reverence his life in the power of its inner purity. The reason is rather in principle to assure the reality of the Incarnation: without sinning the sinless Christ became conclusively and organically dominant in the normal human being, Jesus. Jesus was real and fully one of us. He had no artificial childhood and growth. He learned, even to be good, through teachers and experience. In such a man God won history's decisive victory. Through him sin, law and death were lit up and seen for what they were, and conquered both in a particular life and in universal principle.

In such a man God's nature and purpose to create and redeem became fulfilled even while man's nature and destiny became organically disclosed and enacted. Incarnation is central to our understanding of both God and man. We start our understanding with Christ Jesus as God's authentic presence in a genuine human being. All of life and the very reason for its being must be understood from this point. The center of history runs at the place where God and man meet in organic completeness. The hopes, judgment, forgiveness and creative newness of the lives of all of us are tied together organically with this event. For this reason we dare not forfeit the fullness of the Gospel to an inadequate theology which finds support in some verses of the Bible and explains away the others. Incarnation must not be limited either in the life of Jesus or in its organic meaning and power for all lives. The sinlessness of Jesus is an Umbrella which keeps away from us the truth that God longs to become organically incarnate in us—that the Light of the Sun is for us all. Christ is in us "the hope of glory" even though we are not sinless.

But theology did still more damage. It fitted Jesus into the Jewish sacrificial system, trying to domesticate the Sun within the House of Legality! The sacrificial system made law our ultimate relation to God. Jesus—as presented in the Epistle to the Hebrews—was even made into the high priest of the system! The disciples upon leaving the House of Legality had to have their Umbrella wide open. Imagine it! In their minds, the love of God existed to satisfy their law! To be sure, the Epistle to the Hebrews is not a House of Legality but an Umbrella. It bids us come boldly to the throne of grace and elevates faith to a very high pinnacle. The law remains, nevertheless, the standard for becoming righteous, even when the jubilant cry goes up that the burden of the law has been removed once for all. The God of love needs no placating, no offering once for all to satisfy Him. The prodigal needs no elder brother to come between him and his father with a ransom. The younger brother has only to come to himself, repent, humbly and lovingly accept the father's free and direct forgiveness and be willing henceforth to live responsibly on the father's terms for the family.

The parable of the prodigal son is the heart of Jesus' Evangel, his main view of God; but Christian theology could not accept it, for God would then come too close for comfort. It constructed, instead, an Umbrella to keep away the bright sunlight of God's love. By doctrines insisting on a bloodthirsty God—that is, that He required Jesus' death before He could allow Himself to love us, so that He even sent His son basically to die—Christian theology effectively denied that God as God, the Father Himself, is naturally and eternally love. It built an Umbrella to keep the Sun from shining directly to a world which, however much it may shun the Sun, sorely needs it. "Christian" theology became an ally with the world in denying the naturalness of the love of God.

At the same time theology used the love motive in God's sending Jesus and in Jesus' giving his life for us. The writers could not feel happy in the House of Legality, knowing as much as they did about the Sun. But they satisfied themselves with the indirect sunshine under the Umbrella and around it. Actually, their doctrine of the work of Christ both expressed and denied the love of God. It was not enough for those under the Umbrella that Jesus' dying showed the heart of God and opened the way to life in the Light. They could not or would not understand His holiness and justice as functions of His Love, His very Self in action against sin. They had to construct a doctrine of God where law was equal to and could permanently defeat His Love.

So also with the Resurrection! God was not thought intentionally to use death within His creative purpose. It had to be interpreted as man's worst enemy and as the wages of sin. God was seen through the heavy haze of fear, and theology was written in this murky atmosphere. Nor could God raise men to life after death, in this kind of theology, if it were not for some miraculous encounter of Jesus with death and some cosmic overcoming of it. The reason for this was that ideas from the Mystery Religions got sucked into the Christian interpretation of death and resurrection. We cannot blame the early disciples, of course, for their occasional confusion when confronted with such a revolutionary life and thought. They naturally fell back on the thought worlds of their times. The fact remains, however, that instead of a confident acceptance of the love of God and a daring venture into the Sunlight, the early Christian thinkers constructed themselves an Umbrella wherein the love of God became limited to, and dependent upon, the human-historical enactment of God's love. Nor have later generations dared to accept confidently the compelling implications of Jesus' life and teachings. We are still staying under our Umbrellas.

The doctrine of the Second Coming became, perhaps, the darkest of all the Umbrellas. It completely shut out the living God, embracing and reconciling all men within His eternal time and power. Instead, the doctrine of the Second Coming denied the concept, as Jesus stated it, of God's being love, for all mankind would be extinguished or tormented forever except the few who would escape punishment through faith in the merits of Jesus. It seems doubtful that Jesus ever taught such a doctrine. If Jesus himself held such a view, there is a curious, but understandable division between his revolutionary understanding of God as love and the implications of that love. Such a state is not impossible, for great seers and scientists seldom see all the involvements of their main discovery. It is also possible that he never dealt with the topic of last things in the way of philosophic prediction, but spoke only in terms of practical parables referring to actual life now. Again, it may be that he himself saw and accepted the implications of his radical faith, but knew that the disciples who had not in their own lives the same original power of love and insight into God's nature could not then bear the full truth. It may even be that he tried to tell them and that they misunderstood and misinterpreted his teachings. We do not know.

By the middle of the twentieth century, however, Christian theologians have had time to pray and to think through the implications of the universal love of God. The news of God that should ultimately be wholly good is, nevertheless, still warped, distorted and denied by the violent attempt to hide and to alter the love of God by means of doctrines concerning last things which came out of a narrow Jewish nationalism and an unchristian invidiousness. Here we have a most damagingly arrested development in the Christian faith. Actually, of course, this doctrinal miscarriage is not so much a conscious as a subconscious hiding from the full light of the Sun. Light brings judgment and men prefer darkness to light. The full Light, they feel, is too brilliant to be true. They dare not wholly trust God to be entirely good.

Those of little faith use such phrases as "the love of God," thus declaring themselves to be in the Light, whereupon they then twist the phrases in such a way as actually to deny the meaning of the affirmation. Even today, world-famous Christian leaders argue that we must define the love of God in terms of the New Testament, then affirming, on that basis, that God's love is entirely different from ours, since God alone can prove His love for His children by permanently punishing them in hell! To affirm the inescapably serious holiness of God is as necessary as the Christian faith; to reduce the wisdom and power of God's love to the measure of our human hardness of heart, however, is to make a god in our own image. No, the sovereign Lord is saving Love, and shall win His full victory within His own eternal time.

We poor human beings! How we play fast and loose with words! It is terrible to contemplate, however, that Christian theology should be used to hide God from men; that we ourselves should be building and repairing Umbrellas to keep out the Sun.

We shall never be able effectively to tell the good news of God and from God until that news is really good. As long as we deny by implication what we state by affirmation and repudiate with some teachings what we proclaim by others, we had better not claim to have any Evangel. We stand in God's way, hiding Him from the people. We fight because of our faithlessness the truth which the world needs. Jesus has consequently become a problem and not a power, a wall and not a door, a substitute for God and not a mediator. We call him "Lord, Lord" and deny the very center of his lordship: his making God known and available to humanity.

Modern theology is rampant with idolatry. Even the World Council of Churches is, in fact, denying the Christ when it makes central not the Anointer but the anointed, not the One who raised Jesus from the dead but the one who was raised, not the Sender but the one sent. To call Jesus God is to substitute an idol for Incarnation; to call him Savior, in the ultimate sense, is to deny that all salvation comes from God our Savior and from Him alone in order that God might be all in all. Jesus is savior only by virtue of the fact that God was in him reconciling the world to Himself, a saviorhood in which we must all participate in order to be saved.

God who is Love was truly in Jesus, not only as an influence, a purpose or a moral will, but actually as Godhood; God Himself was in Jesus. God in Jesus was the Christ, God united organically with a fully ordinary human being. Jesus knew full well that of himself he could do nothing; that no one was good but God, that in the realm of ultimate and final things the Father alone knew; and as far as we can now gather, he said so. How often and fully he made this clear we unfortunately do not know. Such sayings would obviously be an offense to the devout attempt of the insecure to substitute Jesus for God in order to have a concrete, intimate picture of Him and not to have to live by faith in the Spirit. Only in such living, however, in the eternally direct relationship with the father, does the prodigal ever fully return.

God was actually in Jesus and through him the light came to shine as a life full of grace and truth. Jesus was God's life in the life of men. Through Jesus the eternal purpose of God was completed conclusively, to found and to fulfill His community—the fully open community of love within the reality of the Spirit of the Living God. Jesus is the way, the truth and the life in that through him came the life of God within which alone the life of man is made real and full. Any definition of man apart from God is falsely abstract; any definition of the fulfillment of man apart from the kind of life of God in Jesus—the divine *Agape*, the New Testament kind of love symbolized and summarized by the Cross and the Crown —is both lacking and wrong. Here is a cornerstone which, although rejected by builders generally, God has Himself laid; and no other kind of cornerstone can ever be laid. In this sense Jesus is our Lord and Leader, but never in the sense that he as a human being is God. God is God. In Jesus God was God and humanity was humanity, and eternally they are different. The created remains created, never becomes God.

The organic culmination in Jesus of the divine and human was the natural fulfillment of both God and man. When God becomes man, so runs my thesis, both God's purpose and man's destiny are fulfilled. The eternal Purpose of God is then to indwell and to fulfill man; the deepest need of man's created nature is to be filled full by God. This alone is the meaning of the Incarnation which is not idolatry.

God alone is to be worshiped. He is the Sun; He alone is the original, uncreate Light, invisible, eternal, in its fullness, ineffable. That Light has entered both human history and the human heart through Jesus. He thereby became the light of the world, as human but not because of his humanity, as God but not by his being God; as making a living way through his blood—God's and man's full self-giving through an actual human being—but not by any priestly offering to placate the Father or to persuade Him to forgive and take back the prodigal; as living victorious over and after death (because that which is born of God cannot be conquered by death but is ever the Death of death) but not by some magic slaying of death in the manner of a mystery religion. Jesus was of the Light and could, therefore, call men into it. He bade men follow him out of the darkness into the Light of the Sun. He is not an Umbrella to come between God and men. He is a way to God whereby we can find Him for ourselves and live in the Sun.

II

An Umbrella Called the Bible

Soon, however, wise men among them said: "We may shortly forget what our Prophet told us about the Sun and how to live in its light. He alone comes from the Sunshine and knows about it. Let us therefore now make for ourselves writings which shall preserve for us and for our children the truths about the Sun." Thereupon they built themselves another Umbrella under the Large One, inside which they recorded the holy testimony of those who themselves knew the Prophet who alone knew the Sun. The holy words recorded, as carefully as possible, what the first followers into the Sun knew about the Prophet, what He had told them about the Sun, and how all who followed Him should live unafraid in its light.

The Bible should not be an Umbrella. The New Testament itself uses, rather, the figure of a light that shines in a dark place until the day itself dawns. The Bible is not so much intended for those who live in the full light of day as for those who live waiting for the day of the new covenant to dawn

38

when men shall know God directly and "shall not teach every man his neighbor" about Him, for they shall all know Him. The Bible should be a means of grace for our imperfect sight, helping us to find our way to heaven and home. As the witness from faith to faith concerning God and His wonderful works, concerning the Christ of God through whom we know the Light and can walk out into it, and concerning those who have walked in the light and found it good—as such the Bible is a help and not a hindrance. The use of the Bible as the final authority for Christian truth is idolatry. Actually it has become a very thick and formidable Umbrella to hide the Sun. How is this possible and how did it happen? How also can the Bible be freed from its abuse and released for its most effective use?

How is it possible for the Bible to be an Umbrella? The Jewish religion relied much on holy Scripture. This was both its strength and its weakness. While Scriptures helped to keep the Jewish people together and encouraged religious living, they also became the occasion for the kind of "Scribism and Pharisaism" which Jesus denounced. Vehemently Jesus opposed "Scribism and Pharisaism" because in circumscribing religious authority to the Scriptures and the traditions, they throttled living religion. Perhaps no other factor as much as his opposition to "Scribism and Pharisaism" led Jesus to the Cross. On the one hand, Jesus found it right and useful to support his teachings by Scripture, while, on the other, he met fanatic opposition as soon as he outspokenly proclaimed that even Moses' words were wrong or insufficient.

Jesus himself, moreover, seems to have lived a good deal with the Scriptures. Possibly this fact became a real problem to him and to his followers. In prayer he found God real and

discovered Him to be radical Love. Part of his inspiration for
this interpretation may have come from pondering Scriptural
teaching and meditating upon great figures in the Old Testament. Some actual words may have been the spark used by
the Spirit to lead him into this new understanding of God and
of his own relation to Him. But some teachings which are
inconsistent with his central understanding of God as love
may be the heritage of his own hearing or reading of Scriptures
and religious literature. The existence of apocalyptic materials
from which his rich imagination drew may account for some
of the elements in his teachings (if they are his) which are
not consonant with the basic drive of his life and vision. Jesus
himself, then, may have been misled as well as helped by the
use of Scripture both outside, in his struggle with Jewish
orthodoxy, and within, in his own creative imagination and
interpretation.

Because of the disciples' intimate association with the Jewish Scriptures, their reporting of Jesus' life and message may
also have been greatly altered. The Jewish Christians tried to
prove that he was the Messiah in terms of their Scriptures.
Jesus may very well have believed so himself, although in a
manner fashioned by his own prayer life and understanding of
the will of God. The Messiah pattern may have been a strong
formative influence in some particular period of his life. We
cannot know with certainty now. But regardless of how much
this idea influenced the thinking of Jesus, the Jewish Messianic expectation is deeply imbedded in the New Testament.

Again and again we hear that Jesus did or said something
"that the Scriptures might be fulfilled," or that this or that
was done according to the prediction of the Holy Writings.
From Jesus' birth in the city of Bethlehem in order to fulfill

Scriptures, to the casting of lots for his garments at his death to justify a prophecy, this is a recurrent theme. The theme is found not only in the Gospel according to St. Matthew, which almost seems written for this purpose, but throughout the New Testament. The material is so plentiful and generally seems so contrived, that the strongest evidence against the reliability of the New Testament as a historic record, particularly concerning the life of Jesus, gathers precisely at this point. It is easy for a critical historian, for instance, to explain why the Bible claims that a nine months' pregnant woman, "an espoused wife," should be taken for a needless hazardous journey, as soon as he knows that the purpose of the writer was to prove that Jesus was born at Bethlehem. It seems entirely likely that Jesus was born in Nazareth, where he lived; but Scripture had to be fulfilled!

We can be fairly sure that the interpretations, also, of the life and teachings of Jesus were warped seriously by the disciples' desire to fit him into the Jewish scheme. By so doing they could appeal to the in-group history of the Jews, thus facilitating communication with, and conversion of, other Jews. A stronger need for this approach was the disciples' need to feel right within themselves, with regard to their own past and their own cultural and religious community. They were convincing themselves that they were not really breaking with Judaism but actually fulfilling it. They tried to have good standing in the House of Legality, not so much, perhaps, with the people there as with their own long-conditioned conscience. Besides, they had no other material in terms of which to interpret their leader, his teachings and his work. How could they go on creatively in the same line as the great original?

Paul and the author of the Gospel according to St. John did a great deal to let the distinctive truth of the Christian faith come to fruition. We marvel at their work. They left the House of Legality almost entirely, except as they took with them the memories of their early loyalties and affections. When they wrote, they interpreted their Leader and his teachings in terms of their earlier background, although to a limited extent and in an indirect way. Paul's own struggle with the Law made him particularly vulnerable; but how much freer he is than the writer of the Epistle to the Hebrews!

We must also remember that law in some form is an inescapable aspect of life and of our relation to God. Although the Light frees us from the laws of darkness and even from the laws by which to get out of the darkness, there are laws for living in the Light. The full Light fulfills the lesser lights of the old ways of living. But the fulfillment which Jesus lived was not clearly seen and felt by the disciples. They, who to some extent were yet inside looking out toward the light, continued to see many of the shadows of the old, familiar darkness.

All this would not have been too serious if the people had kept coming out into the light. Actually they remained partly inside, making to some extent a new legalism out of Christianity. The "Scribes" and the "Pharisees" soon found their exact counterparts inside Christianity. Some actually built a new House of Legality, but most of them were satisfied to make the Bible into an Umbrella under which alone the Sun was to be found. They made the Bible not into a means of grace, but into the final authority for faith. The Bible became not a witness of faith, but an object of faith. One began to believe less in God than in the Bible. Faith in the Bible became presupposed for—and even primary to—faith in God. Without faith in the Bible God could not even be found. Faith in God through the Bible became actually not so much faith in God as faith in the Bible. Thus the Sun could shine only inside the Biblical Umbrella.

Furthermore, this Umbrella came to have many panels. One was the freezing of the past revelation so as to prevent the Light from shining directly on present problems. Instead of mediated immediacy, which characterizes all human knowledge, the believers in the Bible as primary revelation largely stopped with mediated light. The direct personal encounter was no longer of first importance. God became debarred from His own universe. God had spoken once for all. Now He was neither directly needed nor heeded. But He is needed! The Sun must and does keep shining. Communion with God is ever in the present. Mysticism, sacramentalism and pietism, to be sure, were holes in the Umbrella which let in rays of direct Sunlight. But the general attitude was that the Bible was God's finished revelation—that God could no longer make Himself personally known. History is ever a matter of new situations, however, needing present grace; life is ever a matter of present experience, needing immediate communication with God. Whatever the need for mediation, God's revelation must be ever new reality and a present communion.

Another panel in the Umbrella was the freezing of the thought forms and facts of the Bible into literal and final truth. The Hebrews thought that they knew exactly how many generations of men there were since the creation of the world. When modern history disputed such facts, the disputers were called atheists. The modern world generally accepts geological findings but how the Biblicists fought (and still fight) the general idea of evolution! The Biblical world view presupposed the earth to be central in our universe. We now know that we deal with a heliocentric planetary system. How long and bitter was the battle over this issue! Some claim even now in the name of the Bible that the world is flat.

To be sure, few are any longer complete literalists in fact, even though they may be so in idea. A more insidious panel than literalism, therefore, is the freezing of Biblical thought patterns such as the Second Coming, eternal hell, the Hebrew sacrificial system or some particular interpretation of Jesus into eternal truths. There is a general tendency to return to Biblical thinking in the sense of being dependent upon the exact Biblical view for our conceptions of time, of the relation of the Church to the world or of the polity of the Church. The Bible thus used both saps the incentive to find full and concrete interpretation for our day, and blocks the effective acceptance of its own central and eternal truth.

This sophisticated fundamentalism which claims to accept the facts of scholarship, even of Biblical criticism, but which bows only to certain external necessities, like the age of the earth, and accepts scholarship only where it does not upset ecclesiastical applecarts, is a far more serious threat to Christian honesty and effectiveness than is naïve fundamentalism. Both raise the Umbrella which keeps God's truth from shining on them; for they keep insisting that the truth of God must be written inside the Umbrella, rather than seen in the sunshine of personal experience. God's truth, they say, is not self-authenticating, but must always be certified by the Bible. The Bible is thus not a means of grace but the final authority which usurps the place of God. But God refuses to abdicate His revelation and His reign.

Another panel of the Biblical Umbrella was the developing of divisive sects. Group after group has split off from the Christian community on the interpretation of some fragment of the Bible. The wise men dispute among themselves about a book which is in reality a library, and when one of the disputants attracts followers, a new sect is born. In place of the Gospel of universal love comes the growth of limited loyalties bringing with it all the painful result of division and rivalry. Thus the faith of the Christian community is both sapped and denied. It is difficult for the Light to heal those who stay under an Umbrella. A denominationalist is difficult to deal with, for when he is invited into the sunlight he usually defends himself by pointing to some writing inside the Umbrella *which is actually there*. The tragedy is that the Bible is not meant to be "true" in the sense that any and every word can become final authority. Before we can advance the long stretches toward true unity, we must learn to understand the Bible as the witness of faith to faith, remembering all the while that those who witnessed were not miraculously delivered from their own imperfect understanding and seeing. Prejudice, narrowness and divisiveness can, therefore, camouflage their true nature under a zealous loyalty to certain splinters of the Bible.

The words of the Bible are even used to cloak the spirit and implications of the Gospel: another darkening panel of the Umbrella. Those who work on the race front are confronted with the fact that the Bible says that Ham's race was to be forever cursed and the servants of the rest. Those who work on the war front hear that the Bible prophesies wars and rumors of war unto the end. Those who work on the front of general social improvement hear that the Bible dooms the world to become worse and worse. Those who work on the economic front may learn from the Bible that the early Christian community tried socialism and found it wanting, or if they are clergymen interested in economic justice, they may be advised by conservative laymen to stick to the Bible and not bother about what is none of their business. The most tragic fact remains that those who have stressed the Bible most are generally the ones who have been the most socially, politically and economically irresponsible or obstructive. Nor can the most sympathetic claim that "the Bible-belters" have contributed their full share to education and culture. We see, then, how the Bible became an Umbrella and how it is used as such. Unhappily, truth has too often had to fight its way against the zealous supporters of the Bible.

We are concerned with the good news, however—with the Gospel. How can the Bible help without hurting? How can it become a means of grace? How can it be freed from its abuse and released for its effective use? The proper function of the Bible is to lead people into the Light. The Bible is the story of those who walked toward, and in great measure attained, the Light. There is no other Light, ultimately, than God.

The purpose of the Bible, to re-emphasize a point, is to lead people to God. This is a long and difficult task. It is almost impossible for human beings to step directly into the blazing light of the Sun. We must not rebel against being creatures. Earthly existence is of such a nature that we know God mostly in an indirect way. We come to know Him gradually as we appropriate for ourselves the insights of the ages. For the knowledge of the Christian God we need to learn the story of the Christians of all ages who have walked with God. Particularly we need the original story as it became written down in the Bible. Christianity is a story in history as well as an eternal relation. We, therefore, need the night light of the Bible to prepare for the dawn of our direct relation with God. We cannot cut ourselves off from the past where our roots are.

We must, rather, grow deep into the past, if we are to shoot branches and flowers into the Sun and if we are to bear the fruit of the Spirit. We cannot dispense with the Bible as the background of faith, any more than the early disciples like Peter and Stephen could preach to the Jews or understand the fullness of the faith for themselves without going back as a starting point to God's wonderful works with Abraham and Moses. The Bible has a positive part to play as the story of the faith witnesses to the Light, particularly to remind us of him who first knew himself to be of the Light and who led us out into it. We are part of a community, the people of God, and the Bible is a needed focus of history, of communication and of common loyalties and affections.

The story of the original faith witnesses, however, should not leave us at this focus of history but help us forward toward heaven and home. Our God is a living God, a present help in trouble and the companion who understands. The central Biblical story of Jesus should be read that we may have fellowship with a brother who, once having shown us the way to the Father, has thereby—once for all—enabled us to find our own way home. Once we know, we cannot deny what we have seen for ourselves. The Father becomes too real and omnipresent to require a placator or mediator. We need not go back into the past except in gratitude, acceptance and confirmation. Beyond the Father and home, of course, we can never get, but there is always opportunity for fuller exploration of the Father's heart and the home's dimensions.

The Bible should be a draft in the furnace of our spiritual life, and not a damper. It should not stifle but stimulate progress. Or, to change the metaphor, the Bible should not be a brake on social relations, a telling us not to do this or to have that, so much as the clutch of the car, by means of which and by the grace of God we keep shifting our solutions into higher gears. God Himself is shifting the larger gears of history into superhigh with the unlocking of atomic and hydrogen energy, and with cybernetics to extend the means of our thinking as tools once extended the use of our hands. We need new dimensions of interpretation for the days ahead. The Gospel is wider than the reaches of even Hoyle's astronomy, but we try to tie its message down to the thought forms of the ancient world. God is far greater and more real than we dare to imagine.

God wants to deliver the Bible from the dry bones of orthodoxy and to kindle by it the fires with which to light the Church of the Living God. God wants to dissolve the attitudes of moralism, legalism and sheer obscurantism which are connected with Bible worship. The reason that the Bible is worshiped is partly because it is a respected means for justifying and preserving these attitudes.

We can help God deliver the Bible from a cramped orthodoxy by reshaping doctrines so as to make them consistent with the Light. Doctrine should express the purpose of God in the life of man, and the nature and destiny of man in the life of God. Doctrines should not be fixed formulas to be externally accepted and blindly obeyed. They should be the ever-new interpretation of the Light by ever-new faith witnesses who have come to the Light. All accumulations of insight are subject to revision and enlargement. God as Love always sovereignly precedes our understanding of Him and His ways; and to all eternity we can never catch up with Him. Those who have come out of darkness to live in the Light should tell what they see. Then they should also labor to bring news of the Light to those who are in Houses and under Umbrellas. They must learn how best to win all to the living in the Light.

The Bible can help us if the love of God which is central to the whole story is actually allowed to be the basis of interpretation. If this love, as centrally expressed in the Bible, is the nature and purpose of God, what more do we need? Incredible beyond words seems the fullness of the vision that God cares completely and always for all; that all is best in His hands; that He waits only for us to accept His love freely and fully; that even beyond death we meet the same God. What more do we need?

We need to hear this same story over and over again in the experience of those who first knew it, in the experience of those who continued to know it and in the story of our own day—hear over and over again the witness to the faithfulness of God. Particularly do we need the reassurance of this central message of the Bible, inasmuch as most of the time we unfortunately see more of the night light than the dawning of the new day. But the most important choice is to live by the Light as fully as possible. The more we do so, the more we can see that the full light in the Bible is the love of God, and we can use our new sight to inform those who live by faith in the Bible rather than in God Himself and thus lead them to the Light. For theirs is the sight of the letter, which kills, not the faith of the Spirit, who saves.

The Living Word, on the other hand, which became flesh,

will illumine the Word which is written, and will use this Word to meet the needs of all, whatever their degree of darkness. In the full Light, the light which shone in Jesus and now shines in the Spirit, we can distinguish between what is light and darkness in the Bible. Thereby doctrine becomes the living Word to living men. Thereby the Bible becomes dependent upon our living in the Spirit. Thereby the Bible fulfills the past and helps guide us into God's better future. Thereby the Bible can be read as a help and not a hurt, as a power not of the conglomerate past but of the Spirit, who is the Light in the past, the present and the future.

That Light, too, explains most fully the total meaning of life. We do not have to run around in a first and second century museum nor in a private garden walled off from the rest of the world. The Bible is not the private possession of some in-group; it is not intended for esoteric worshipers. The Light is the Sun, and all light comes therefrom. Our task is, rather, to explain how from the Sun came the coal, oil and wood which are burned in the Houses. These are still indirect forms of light from the Sun. For those who have found the Light, there is practically no temptation to return to the other lights nor to claim out of false tolerance that these indirect lights are as original or as bright as the Sun.

Those who know the Sun long both to lead men into the Light and to explain to all that we live in a universe where all light comes from the Sun. They know full well that we do not live in pluriverses where our light is true for us, while all other lights are false and have nothing to do with our Sun. All indirect lights, they see, must be explained as dependent upon the Sun although these lesser lights can never take its place either as original Light or in brilliance. There is no adequate comparison between the power of the direct Light and all indirect lights.

Thus we are delivered both from a false narrowness and a false tolerance by living in the Light. We are freed from being a group desperately clinging to the sheer faith acceptance of the story of the Prophet as our only hope, to become instead the people of the Prophet who live in His light, seeing that His is the final light in terms of which all other lights must be understood. We understand, too, that the purpose of all other lights is to prepare for and lead people to live in the light of the Sun. If the Bible is used in this way it does not take the place of the Sun but becomes the light in the night that looks forward to the dawning of the new day, when even its own important light will be fulfilled. It will, in fact, be fulfilled by being no longer needed by those who live in the direct light of the day.

If the Bible is thus interpreted through the love of God, its own highest peak, it cannot become an Umbrella over the divisiveness within the Christian community. Although we recognize that we have to live as creatures, not as pure spirits, and therefore need the help of Scriptures and institutional religion, all Scriptures are themselves under the criterion of the love of God. They must, therefore, be used within the direction and the power of the unifying Spirit. The Spirit produced a variety of manifestations. There is no false sameness wherever He works, but, on the contrary, there is ample room for creative difference and individual expression. All doctrines, creeds, polities, histories and ordinances which divide become serious but secondary to the one essential unity within the love of God: the very Light which began its bright shining into history in Jesus, and is the distinguishing characteristic of the people of God. The Bible does not then become the occasion for conflicting in-groups, but rather the occasion for creative variation within the unity of the Spirit. Within the bond of perfectness the love which casts out all fear makes for true peace.

The Bible becomes, too, the incentive for the transformation of the world according to the pattern of God and by the power of love. The Christian community knows full well that its fellowship with God in love, trust and obedience is central to its being. It knows that the Kingdom of God cannot come by means of the mere improving of social patterns, however skillfully and wisely. Men must be born again to see the Kingdom of God and they must live within the power of the Spirit if they are to live in love with one another. To live in the light and power of God's love is to know that all creation is His, that all men belong to Him potentially, that He is the Lord of history, and that therefore Christians must be the salt of the earth. Those living in the Light become eyes for those living in the shadows. They also must heed the radical concern which they feel toward all men to help them to the full extent of their needs. The Bible thus helps both to make us human and to care for humanity. The use of the Bible to bolster reactionary social forces is discredited and the Bible becomes not the preserver but the eliminator of the darkness in the world.

The Bible should be a main means of grace, used for God's glory and for human help. We do not honor the Bible by worshiping it, by making it into an Umbrella under which to try to find the Light. The Bible should be, rather, the highway to heaven, the road into the Light. Only by our own coming out from under the Umbrella to find God's love real for ourselves, can we find the right meaning and use of the Bible. When we do this, it becomes not a problem, but a power; not the Light by which we judge all other lights, but the useful night light which awaits the coming of the dawn. As long as we need the light in a dark place, let it shine, bright and beautiful, and let us thank God for its true and steady rays. But when the dawn comes, let us not weep because its light has been fulfilled and because in the light of the Sun we can no longer see by it alone! The Sun is the Light to which the Bible witnesses. To call the Bible faithful is to heed its finest light and come out into the Sun. The light in a dark place first leads us to the prophet of the Light; our prophet leads us out into the Sun.

III

An Umbrella Called the Church

But even their wisest men disputed among themselves concerning what the words which were written inside the new Umbrella meant and who had the right to interpret them, whereupon they set about gradually to construct a third Umbrella, inside the second, which they called the Church. On the under side of this new Umbrella they wrote: "Gather here all who want to accept the Prophet who came from the Sun and taught us to live in the Sun. We are the true SUNWORSHIPERS. Outside this Umbrella no one can be sure of the Sun, nor that it truly lights, warms and heals us. We know only Him and what the writings tell of Him as these are authoritatively interpreted for us by those under this Umbrella called the Church. Come under this Umbrella all ye who want to live in the light of the Sun. We are the true SUNWORSHIPERS."

Nevertheless fear arose. Some did not trust even the teachings of the savants under the Church. Even the large Umbrella plus both the others could not make them feel secure about the Sun. They said: "Let us now interpret the writings for ourselves to arrive at the original words of our Lord and Leader.

54

Let us accept Him only and what He did for us and taught us."
Some of these made themselves smaller Umbrellas inside
which they wrote formulas, called creeds, concerning that
which was really important in the original writings and kept
repeating these formulas about the Prophet who came from
the Sun and told them to come out to live in the light of the
Sun. Others picked out this saying or that for their little Umbrellas as the most important clue to understanding and the
most obedient way of accepting the Prophet and his message
concerning their living in the Sun. . . .

Ideally the Church is the community of the children of
God, where the sons live in the presence of the Father. The
family does not take the place of the Father, but exists in
direct relation to Him. But the Church took on the function
of an Umbrella to the degree in which the Father was for-
saken, deemed far away or treated as an absentee Ruler rather
than as the central, most intimate Member of the family who
understands the children far better than they understand Him.
The family became, in effect, the substitute for the Father, the
members sufficing for each other, shutting him out.

How, historically, did the Church become an Umbrella?
In the first place, when Jesus was gone, much reliance was
placed on the Holy Spirit and on prophecy, new and old. The
early Church really relied on the Spirit as the guide both of
individuals and of the corporate people of God. God was
immediate to them, in them. Observe the nature of the phrases
they used: "God stood by me," "The Spirit testified to me,"
"The Spirit did not allow us." The power of the early evangelists was the power of God in human history. No wonder
the Spirit testified constantly to His own grace and that the

disciples were multiplied. No wonder the believers dared not only to confess a despised message but also to face the consequences of their testimony even unto death. Christ was the Spirit, not Jesus after the flesh. He was the risen Lord, the eternal Word, who was from the beginning with God and was God. Theological formulations differed, but the God of the Cross and of the Resurrection, the God of the New Age and of the New Community, the God of all power and comfort, the God of Love Himself, was personally present.

As masses were converted, however, and as the Gospel spread more extensively than intensively, was experienced more secondhand and less firsthand, was exemplified more in the ordinary man and confined less to the heroes and saints of the faith, abuses arose: abuses of life, of faith, of the interpretation of prophecy and of the witness of the Spirit. Persecution also pressed upon the generality of believers the need for some definite rules of faith. Those who were missionaries, furthermore, needed a common Christian message. False prophets arose, both on the side of law and of license. The spread of the faith required more organization. The Jewish pattern of Scriptural authority and of authoritative organization which permeated the disciples' experience helped to direct the growth of the Christian Church toward institutional rigidity. Thereupon institutional religion gradually grew not only into a protest against individualistic religon, false fervor and irresponsible leadership, but also into a defense against vibrantly creative, personal faith. Organizations develop in this pattern. Thus no conscious defect or cunning manipulation weakened the personal relation to God which was the strength and victory of those who first followed the Master, but rather the exigency of events.

Both leaders and people became increasingly affected by the growth of the Church and its responsible life. The leaders focused more and more attention on the needs of the Church and the people became increasingly dependent on the leaders. Thus step by step, with no special design, the Church grew into an ever more powerful organization. Unintentionally the Church, weakened by *its lack of primary focus on the will of God for the immediate present*, became shaped into an Umbrella. Under this Umbrella its leaders were to claim that the Holy Spirit was given once for all on Pentecost to the Church, that God expresses Himself not through individuals but through the Church, that the Bible must be interpreted authoritatively and that even the Second Coming was nothing but the coming of the Spirit and the founding of the Church. These statements are all relatively true, and profoundly important; but not *wholly* true, and therefore profoundly dangerous.

Consider, for one example, the theme of the preceding chapter: the case of the Scriptures in the context of the Church. Such consideration will show how the second Umbrella in our parable actually covers the third and the smaller Umbrellas of the creeds and the sects. In one sense the Church grew from the Scriptures and could not have been fashioned as it was apart from them. In another sense, of course, the Jewish community had existed before the Scriptures and the Scriptures could not have been written as they were apart from that Jewish community. In one sense the Church wrote the Bible, making the Bible secondary to the life which created it; but, in another sense, it wrote the Bible with reference to previous Scriptures and became itself formed by the new Scriptures. Above both Scriptures or community, however, brooded the Spirit who inspired whatever truth they expressed, the truth by which they were written. The Bible and the Church, therefore, stand together under the same judgment and exist within the same authority who is neither an absentee Landlord nor even an absent Father except as He is deserted by His own children. The Sun shines over both Umbrellas!

Consider this development as illustrated by an example from secular history. How did Communism arise? Karl Marx wrote *Das Kapital*. The first Communist community was pitifully small but passionately convinced of its truth and willing to suffer for it. What founded Communism: Marx, *Das Kapital*, or the convinced Communist community? The answer is that all three did. Economic history and the needs of a new world, plus the awakening of the masses within a new kind of world community and communication, were the preconditions for the founding, even as Marx had foreseen. This was the Communist fullness of time. Whatever degree of truth is contained in Marx's claim to be scientific is found in his concept of the nature of history and its stage of technological development. Faith in *Das Kapital* (which very few understand) has been of enormous significance to the pulsing power of the movement. Even so, under the stress of practical needs the Communist community has altered its doctrine through compromises and accommodations. The partisans of the original "gospel" have now for some time been dangerous heretics and often liquidated. Communism has no ultimate metaphysics to defend. The existential nature of Communist doctrine has, of course, facilitated practical adjustment. The community, although not free from division and conflict on account of theory, was thus not basically hampered by doctrine.

Much in the same way and for the same reason, the Church

through its institutional channels assumed more and more the right to interpret and to apply Scripture. But, as previously mentioned, its reliance on Scripture has, nevertheless, handicapped it throughout its history. The great alienation of modern man would very likely never have taken place if the Church had been flexible to truth, instead of fighting bitterly the progress of science in the name and authority of the Bible as interpreted by the Church. This struggle between the authority of science and the authority of the Scriptures has been going on for hundreds of years and, even now, many young people grow up with one view of the world propounded in school and another in the Church while neither is adequate for the fullest truth. Thus, the Church became an Umbrella in its allegiance to the Bible as the ultimate standard of Truth, substituting a mixed message concerning the Sun for exposure to the Sun Himself.

Another way in which the Church became an Umbrella was by usurping the function of the Holy Spirit. Through the Holy Spirit Jesus gave commandments to his apostles. Over and over again he stressed that he of himself could do nothing and that the truth which he taught was not his own but the Sender's. The Acts of the Apostles abounds in emphasis on the personal presence, work, guidance and power of the Holy Spirit. He who was to lead the disciples into all truth and let them do greater works than had been done even by Jesus, actually was powerfully present in spite of all the human faults of the early witnesses to the faith. Therefore, the Word was preached and lived with power and the Christian community grew in numbers and influence.

But individualistic excesses, deviations and peculiarities discredited, to a considerable degree, reliance on the Holy Spirit.

No one acquainted with history should underestimate the dangers of individualism or of splinter groups which claim direct dependence on the Holy Spirit. The Church has had to face severe strains and conflicts on account of a false spiritism. Because of these shortcomings the organization tended to take the place of the work of the Holy Spirit. Defects of personal faith became the occasion for minimizing the work of the Spirit. Subtly, gradually, graspingly the institution began to feel that the Spirit had come, once for all; that any manifestation of Him had, therefore, to be in line with His conclusive manifestation in the Church; that the Church enacted such manifestation in its corporate leadership according to Scripture and Council. In this way the powerful work of the Holy Spirit as the direct, present activity of God in human life and history became increasingly thwarted or tamed down in interpretation to a new Scribism and Pharisaism. Christianity as closed in by the Church became a legalism more like a House than an Umbrella. In confining the Holy Spirit the Church went a long way in shutting the door on God. Pentecost became a date on the calendar instead of a constantly recurring experience.

From this point on, ecclesiasticism had a natural entree and welcome. Salvation deteriorated, in a large measure, from personal repentance before God to a form of ecclesiastical insurance through rites and privileges administered by the institution. Subtly, below the level of conscious choice, the people came to depend more upon the Church than upon God. Somehow the Church made things right with Him. The creative power of special providence through the individual in the closed closet, or through two or three gathered together with Christ in their midst, became obstructed underneath the reliance upon the power politics of ecclesiastical assemblies which clamped chains of creeds around the growing body of the young Christian community.

This plight was in part due to the fact that the latter disciples lacked the immediacy and depth of the earlier disciples. This state of affairs was also dependent upon the subtle substitution of dependence on the authority of the Church for reliance on the personal presence and power of the Holy Spirit who concretely fashions new directions for new situations and keeps on making all things new. Thus the past became a frozen decision in the present, by means of which the Holy Spirit was prevented both from functioning and from being heeded when He did break through in Spirit-led individuals or groups. In this way, also, the Church became an Umbrella.

The third way is really an aspect of the first two. The first was the substitution of the Church for the Holy Spirit as the final authority in the interpretation and use of the Scriptures. The second was the domestication of the Holy Spirit within the control of the Christian community. The third way in which the Church became an Umbrella was by its stress on the work and reality of the Church as primary to the individual. The Church became the agent of salvation for the individual. But God works equally through persons and people. He wants both fellows and fellowship, and neither can take the place of, or be primary to, the other. In one real sense the fellowship comes first through persons, i.e., through individual or personal experience. The Christian experience is of God, of the Holy Spirit, of the Christian community, but comes in and through individual understanding, repentance, appropriation and enactment. At an Institute of Religious and Social Studies someone congratulated a Roman Catholic leader on the fact that many Catholics practice personal prayer and devotions and through them find God genuinely real. The reply was unexpected. "Yes, I know. We must stop this Protestant heresy or else we will soon have no need for the Church!"

In this respect most Protestants are Catholics! Few practice the personal prayer life with depth and perseverance to the intensity where God becomes personally present and special providence becomes convincingly demonstrated. Kierkegaard saw with prophetic clarity this nominal Christianity which was partly sustained by the rationalization of its paid advocates. Neither crowd nor community can take the place of the closed closet, the early morning watches, the daily commitment and worship, the individual prayer without ceasing. No matter how completely social the Christian experience is, in its content, it is always, when real and full, as personal and direct an experience as the daily living and companionship of a man and his wife.

Although this experience also is social, nevertheless there is, even in this intimacy of years of living together, no way in which the one can enter into the precise experience of the other. There is an inviolable privacy about personal experience, however social the relation. There is also an immediacy of confrontation apart from which all corporate experience loses its edge and reality. In Christian experience this confrontation is with God; unless perchance Christianity as a religion be defined as secondhand, as standing between God and man. To a large extent the Church has, in fact, done just that and has thereby become an Umbrella in the way of the Light. People have more contact with the Church than with God; it is more real than He; whereas the Church should first be real in God and only then God real through the Church.

The fourth way in which the Church became an Umbrella was by shackling men's consciences to creeds. Creeds whenever they are considered to be authoritative for faith, explicitly or implicitly, are metaphysical and historical statements imposed on the present by the past. The heart of the creeds may very well be true; they may point in the right directions; but they work to kill living faith. Only rugged personal faith can keep from being choked by creeds. Firsthand religion tends always to become enfeebled and distorted by creeds. They are the works of the "Scribes" and the "Pharisees." They are sure evidence of secondhand religion. They are Umbrellas within the Umbrella. If the God of history is so unreal that He has to be nailed down by creeds, it is better to let Him go. If the metaphysical affirmation is so tenuous that only by external indoctrination can the belief be induced, the affirmation has little living value or reality.

When God is personally real to the point of fear and trembling or of humble acceptance, there is no need for creed. Substitutes for God crowd Him out and make Him unreal. Churches that have gone to sleep spiritually or live on inherited capital might as well mumble creeds. A few worshipers may have intellectual scruples, but most people in repeating a creed either are not thinking of what they are saying, or have never fought enough either with history or with ultimate truth to have deep misgivings.

Creeds by their very nature and function are the signs and tokens of the worship of a faraway God. They witness to the spiritual poverty of the Church that uses them. But the way is broad and many travel it. Narrow is the way that leads to life, because we have to travel it single file. The Christian community is real fellowship, but we can never enter it except one by one and we can never maintain it except through the constant use of the closet with the shut door.

The fifth way in which the Church became an Umbrella was through the choice of a particular Gospel teaching as the best way to understand the Christian revelation, or the choice of a particular practice as the best way to obey the Lord, and then making this teaching or that act of obedience the crucial test of our relation to God. It was pointed out already in the last chapter how the Bible became the ground for divisiveness. The same tendency may be observed from the perspective of the Church. *The combination of the Bible and the Church* is crucial for the understanding of the Umbrellas which separate us from God. Not all denominationalism arose from the interpretation of Bible passages, but much, very likely most, of it did, when some leader fixed attention on some special Bible teaching. Subtly this particularistic stress became the basis of an in-group which considered itself the True Church or the Right way. Thereupon this in-group lashed out to denounce others, or condescended to admit the superiority of its own certainties and securities. Thus was born a divisive denomination that not only individuates the faith but robs it of its power as the community *whose very nature it is to open communications*, to break down barriers and to foster the inclusive fellowship in Christ.

Many gentle and loyal spirits have devoted a misguided zeal for Christ to crucify Him afresh in the actualities of Church life. Faith in the Umbrella and complete attention to its nature have made them miss the Light of the Sun, the very light which they profess and intend to love. Scripture verses, rites of the Church, even names, have been the occasion for divisive and destructive sectarianism. Behold with pained astonishment how the Church, the open community in Christ, has become an Umbrella! No weeping of Jesus over Jerusalem can be more deep and tragic than the weeping of his true followers over the Church which bears his name.

How, then, can we now restore the Church to a Christian community or—if the name "Christian" has been spoiled by history—to the Church of the Living God? How can the Church become the kind of community which shall not only proclaim but actually enact the good news of the Gospel of the Universal God? Can the Church once again become an evangel with the power of Pentecost? Can it so enact its own true nature, that it must live and reach the world in all its needs to tell it clearly, urgently, insistently the good news of God?

God's good news in Christ is at its heart communal. Love is an outreaching relation of persons. Christian love is a relation of persons within the inclusive love of God. This fellowship is central. It is a creative community within the ongoing work of God in creation and redemption. It is an existential response to God. It is a direct relationship in the Spirit. As such it transcends any previous manifestation of its own life and witness and stands judge over all its past deliverances. It is the community of God's present truth for present need. It is the society of God's concrete guidance and empowerment. In this sense the Church is the judge of the Bible; the living Word, of the written word. If we are to have only Umbrellas then the Prophet needs to be validated by the Bible and the Bible to be interpreted by the Church. Such procedure is thoroughly consistent with the needs of history. The logic of the Roman Catholic Church is unassailable, provided that there is no primary revelation of God in the immediate present. If our faith must be in Umbrellas, let us all return to the Mother Church. If not, let the Reformation continue until we have folded all Umbrellas. Let the Light rule our lives directly. Let faith in God and experience of Him through the Holy Spirit in prayer, faith and community become central to the Christian faith. Then in the Light, we can see the use of the Bible in the Church, the place for the Church itself and the rules of faith by means of which we appropriate our historic heritage.

Even such a dynamic approach, to be sure, may seem externalistic to a vital believer who knows God through first hand experience. A man may have received numerous love letters from his wife long before their marriage. If their relation is right and real, he does not need to keep rereading these letters in order to know that his experiences of his wife are real. He need not examine continually his present understanding of her in the light of her past utterances. Her contemporary words need not be criticized in the light of her past words to see if the messages are still truly from her. Indeed, if estrangement takes place he may prefer her letters to her present words. If love grows cold, he may hold up the original love letters as a norm. If he becomes mentally ill and she seems unreal to him, or if he only worshiped an idea or an ideal of her in the first place, he may indeed withdraw into her past communications.

Otherwise his main business of living is in the present. On some quiet Sunday afternoon he may well get out her old letters and be thoroughly refreshed and rekindled by the recalling and reliving of a deep and dear past. The more he loves her, the more everything in her past will be precious and significant, but she is still the center of attention and affection. He needed the period of courtship to come to his present relation. The past must be accepted, honored, appropriated and appreciated. But true love lives in the present.

So also the life of the Church lives within the present love of God. What God has done in the past is immeasurably precious and enriching to recall. The contemporary situation could not exist apart from the effective past. The Bible should, therefore, be interpreted in the present according to the power and light of the Spirit, not as external authority judging the present, but as the occasion for the continuous appropriation of the past in the living present. The use of the Bible by the Church thus becomes a means of constant grace, not a substitute for our knowledge and love of God in the living Spirit. In the utterances from the past, too, there will be found the same faithful and life-giving voice. What He has done up to now is a source of gratitude and togetherness. But God Himself is ever the real companion. He is personally, presently real, and nothing in the past can begin to be so real and so important that He should Himself be judged real or present by it.

If the wife should die, the lonely widower might well spend much time with her precious letters and relive their companionship through actually seeing her words and concretely picturing her deeds. If God becomes unreal to us, then truly we must rely on past revelation as primary. If we go away from God, then the record of His mighty deeds has to be substituted for the assurance of His living presence. The Church as the community of the Living God, however, must have a living relation with its Lord and hear ever anew the infinitely tender assurances of its Father. This does not mean—again the point must be vigorously emphasized—that we may disregard or discard the utterances of the past or fail to appreciate the signs of God's past faithfulness; rather, we must put them in their proper place in the light of the reality and significance of God's personal presence now. The Church that lives mostly in the past is not alive and alert to God's present Word for the world. To live mostly in the past is to face death.

The living Church knows that the guarantee of God's presence, as the New Testament testifies, is the gift of the Spirit. The Holy Spirit, God's immediate presence, is the guarantee of the grace of God. The Church will cease being an Umbrella when it resolutely accepts the reality of God's own presence and becomes His living summons to all creatures to come into the Light. Whenever the Church will learn to trust the power of the Holy Spirit to direct its life, whenever the Church will learn that He is a personal agent present in history, whenever the Church will accept and appropriate the truth that it is rooted and grounded in God only when it is itself constituted basically by the personal presence of the Spirit—then and only then will the Church escape being an Umbrella and become evangelical according to its own true nature. Then it will neither dare nor need to domesticate the Holy Spirit and usurp His place by its organization. Then the institution will stand both under present judgment and present radical renewal. Then the Church will change with as much flexibility as the creative newness of human need, while being held steady by the faithfulness of God.

The Church which is built within the love of God is at the same time as strong as a pillar and as fluid as water. The Holy Spirit is structurally as steady as the heart of God and functionally as adaptable as His love. The Church which genuinely accepts the Lordship of the Holy Spirit can never become an Umbrella. It becomes the clear light on the hill of present attainment. But no Church can live this life unless it know the continuous power of Pentecost. Only to those for whom God is more real than they—because the ground of their assurances is not their own feelings, moods or thoughts but the gift of the Spirit—can there be a contemporary community of the grace of God, the Church of the Living God. For such a Church there is only one judgment: the fruits of the Spirit.

Even this judgment, however, is for the outsiders or for those for whom the love of God has grown cold; for in the blazing heat and light of personal confrontation one cannot measure the reality of the experiences by the fruits produced. Similarly one cannot be assured that one's wife is real or still loves by whether or not she keeps cooking good meals and renders the usual signs of endearment. When doubt arises, the relationship is already endangered. The Church of the Living God will produce the fruit of the Spirit, but only because it keeps on being confronted by a Reality which keeps on being its real life.

Similarly the Church guards against individualism. Christian experience is perforce personal, but it is never individualistic. In its own inner structure it is communal. Therefore, wherever the Christian experience is understood and vital there is no individualism. Personal experience is of God, Christ, the Holy Spirit, the Christian community, and through these, unexceptionally and unequivocally, for the whole world. These experiences must, of course, be thoroughly personal, for through such personal experiences the Spirit enriches, empowers and corrects the Christian community. The Church not only permits such immediate personal experiences, but also knows that they partake of its own nature.

Conversely, the Church stands—within the very structure of the Holy Spirit—as the objective corrective of individualism. Since we are frail and faulty human beings, we fail to understand the power and significance of a community of those whom the Spirit continuously enriches. And since we are sinful and far from God, we naturally put ourselves first and thereby destroy or impair this kind of community. Therefore, to speak of Umbrellas only in terms of the false interpretation or appropriation of Jesus, the Bible or the Church is dangerous. By so doing we may forget that all these Umbrellas are constructed by persons. *In one sense the self is the main Umbrella because the self constructs all the Umbrellas in order to hide from the demands of God which seem too costly to fulfill.* External hideouts are, so to speak, prefabricated within, at least in intention. The externals become the occasion for building Umbrellas. The sinful self, therefore, must not be treated as though he would rejoice if the Umbrellas were re-moved *for which Jesus, the Bible, the Church and the Creeds are only the occasions.* Individualism underlies all social attempts to shut God out from man's life. Sin is the main constructor of Umbrellas, personal or social! The Church in itself is impotent to correct this fault or to forgive this sin, except it point and lead the individualist to the Spirit, where power to heal and grace to forgive can be found. Structurally and functionally the Holy Spirit and the Church reinforce each other.

To summarize these points it may be said that the Christian community when it is real worships a living God where all words and deeds from the past are secondary to its life. When, however, religion becomes secondhand, these words and deeds can and should remind the Church of the nature of the original community which so genuinely knew God that it could produce such writings. Besides being the best means for appropriating the past in a living present, the Bible is thus a guard rail to keep the Christian community from going into the ditch of error or slough of lovelessness. It is never, however, the primary or central road to God. It can never be the main approach to the reality of God.

Similarly the organization can test the spirits, whether they be of God, only if it is itself completely in the hands of the Holy Spirit. An organized Church life mitigates and militates against irresponsible individualism. We need the organization. Too often, however, the organization identifies its own past with God's present, thus thwarting the Spirit. In the case of individualism, too, the Church can judge this to be unchristian only if it has allowed all possible room for personal religion, personal prophecy and personal creativeness. Through individuals comes the present voice of God for the present need of people and persons, of the Church and of the world. The only way to cure individualism within the Church, however, is to become a genuine community with the Holy Spirit, wherein are fulfilled both persons and people. Where such community is real, defections from it and externalistic disciplines fall into second place. Our real problem is, always and centrally, a lack of the pulsing reality of the Gospel.

The same position must be taken with regard to creeds. They are Umbrellas hiding the Light. They become substitutes for God. They serve to make people try to live by sight and not by faith, by external authority and not by personal encounter. Even so, for the hardness of our hearts and because of the gullibility of our minds, we human creatures, frail as we are and easily led away from the truth, need some definite statements to guide our thoughts. Our relation to God is never *de novo*. It has historic roots. Our experience is never merely personal. It must have a social history. Our minds do not interpret the universe afresh; they depend upon the cumulative work of the race. Individual faith is ever mediated in content and context by the historic community.

Not to have any statements of faith, therefore, is to court disaster. It is to forfeit our heritage from the past. It is to sell our Christian birthright of objective events and meanings for a mess of superficial subjectivism. It is to barter the steady channel of community life for the shallow swirls of impressionism. It is to give away the midstream of Christian experience for the eddies of shifting immediacies. Creeds, when genuinely and not apologetically accepted, are Umbrellas because they claim to express absolute revelation and demand unquestioning loyalties. They are authoritarian rather than authoritative. They purport to contain formulas of faith necessary for salvation. The rule of faith, which is conceived as content of revelation guaranteed by the Church as an authoritative institution, if accepted, kills genuine faith. But the community has the right and the duty humbly to chart its past voyage, witness to its truest findings and recommend its experience to new voyagers.

Each navigator, in one sense, must begin for himself and learn from the sailing. Christian experience is a matter of steering, of discovering for oneself new lands. If the Church so charts the steering that no personal decisions are involved, the Church robs the navigator of both the very reason for his setting out to sea by divine orders and the personal pleasure of learning to man the craft and to reach goals for himself.

Reality centers in God. God is love. Love gives freedom for

fellowship. Freedom learns through decisions. Decisions depend upon seeing in advance of choice and afterward learning from the consequences of the choices. Seeing is *both communal and personal*. Each man, therefore, begins with contemporary history but he also begins from the beginning in his own life. Statements of faith are the cumulative experience of society. We need these statements. We cannot, in fact, do without them. We need to make them as clear and definite as we can. But never can they take the place of personal finding, individual choices, separate learning. Life is always new and different, to be learned afresh by each spirit.

Creeds, as the condensation of authoritative revelation, kill personal initiative insofar as they impose the experience of the past and induce a prefabricated response rather than suggest a way to truth through the experience of the past. There must be landmarks of truth and history, but no system or formula should do more than point toward them. They can recommend certain ways of steering. But when all is said and done, truth is living. The life is the light of men. And every rich and full life eludes adequate definition and reduction to principles or formulas.

Even the recitation of events becomes external, substitutionary and conducive to religion at second hand. No event can substitute for another event. It can prepare a living way for a following event. It can prepare the way for new conditions, make available new choices, make possible new relations to reality. But each life must be lived for itself in all its real dimensions; it must relate itself, through whatever mediacy, directly to God. No father can give his son his life's wisdom in any simple set of formulas or in any exhaustive treatises. Life at its center is deeper, richer, more complex, more personal, more inwardly real than any and all descriptions or pre-scriptions.

A father should, of course, try to communicate his experi-ences; he longs to share his insights; but the deeper his life, the more surely he knows that his son finally must learn for himself from God and from life, and that only his son's most intimate experiences and his own interpretation of them will have the intimate inner meaning which for him is personal reality. Sim-ilarly, the Church must communicate its chart of experience, but the compass that points to the north star of Reality is in each soul. Each one must personally come to know his God and to follow his own compass. He can use the chart of the Church as a general map indicating the direction in which he ought to sail, but the islands and the seas will yet be new to him.

Or, to change the figure, an individual can get a road map from the Church which points to general destinations. But life is never a concrete highway easily followed. It is ever a territory with parts of the trail purposefully unmarked, for each to find. An authoritarian Church tries by creeds and formulas to mark a perfectly true and safe path to glory, but God will not have it so. His purposes in creation cannot be bypassed without penalty. Creeds give evidence of collective insecurity. The creed is an Umbrella. Yet the statement of faith, as the witness of past experience to ever-new experience, performs the task which the creed is meant to do, but does not tie the individual down to a routine or even possibly to a dishonest lisping of what externally has to be believed. The creed is the essence of orthodoxy; it is the final concentration of "Scribism and Pharisaism." It is the epitome of religion at second hand. Certainly one can be Christian and repeat creeds, but the saying of them if not objectionable is at best irrelevant. Mature faith repudiates creeds not only as the playpen of the past, but as the false possessiveness of parental control.

Finally, divisive denominationalism is an Umbrella. Loyalty to this saying as the best way to understand or to that act as the best way to obey can camouflage collective selfishness under personal idealism. The inclusive Light is hid from under the exclusive Umbrella. The good news of God for the world is substituted for the narrow rules of a sect. Yet, on this topic, too, we must go deeper in order to find the fuller truth. Most people can live by very few ideas and these must be simple and concrete. Almost anyone can find a following if he is passionately convinced of some concrete truth, be it narrow or wide. Hence sectarianism! If the center of the unifying Christian faith, therefore, is not real enough, simply enough stated and passionately enough held, it cannot keep people together in true community. How can we find a community that is effective for both common and general faith which does not, nevertheless, by its very effectiveness become an Umbrella? The Roman Catholic Church held people together not only by an external organization but by its clear central doctrine of the Church. Protestantism tried the Bible, but this contained too many diverse ideas to serve effectively as the basic unifier of the Church.

The Roman Catholic Church is suffering from the fact that the dome of St. Peter is too heavy. Part of Protestantism is now turning to unity, using the Bible as a convenient reason while actually being motivated by other forces and circumstances. This search for unity is all to the good provided that it does not create a superchurch which usurps the place of personal experience and that of small groups. Realists know that a very few persons, centrally located, can pull all the organizational strings and select the theological patterns. This is particularly true in periods of fluid social patterns and mounting political perplexities. The organization need not be close-knit or externally coercive for this to take place; it need only be extensive and centrally organized. We cannot escape the plain fact, however, that we are human beings who operate in a world of power attitudes and power situations, not as perfected saints. We are hard driven by the natural man in us. Thus the Ecumenical Movement, even though very much needed, can itself easily become a particularly dangerous Umbrella.

Can anything be done about this situation? How can we avoid the kind of centralization that thwarts local and personal initiative and response, on the one hand, and divisive denominationalism, on the other? Both are Umbrellas. Can the Church effectively become the historic center of the Evangel? Can the Church become man's best news from God? Can the Church not only know the claim upon it to be the purpose of God's creation but actually realize that purpose in concrete human history? This is man's hardest question and most difficult task. Answers to these questions will be attempted in the next chapters, facing both the toughness of our human natures and problems, on the one hand, and, on the other, the nature of our Christian resources. If we are to fulfill such a calling to Christian community, we must face candidly the question of evangelism to the Christians. How can our present traditionalistic Churches be converted to the Church of the Living God? Or can they?

IV

Light for Christians

It happened, however, that one of their number began to wonder about the Umbrellas. He read over and over again the words of the Prophet to the effect that they should LIVE in the Sun; that to honor him was to follow him into the sunshine. And so he went forth into the sunshine. At first, to be sure, the Light hurt his eyes and for a while he longed to return under the Umbrellas. As he grew used to living in the light of day, however, he grew happier and happier about it. At last he could no longer bear not to tell his friends under the Umbrellas about his now life in the Sun. He returned with great joy to let his friends know that the Prophet was right. Not only could they leave the dark, old barn with the Lamps of the Law, but they could even leave the Umbrellas— all of them—to live in the Sunlight itself!

They looked at him with mingled feelings of hope and fear, of temptation and resistance, of near-belief and hurt. At last they cried out, however, "You dishonor our Prophet! You scorn our Umbrellas! Apart from him and apart from these we know no Sun, whether it can help us and whether we can live in its light." The young man who had himself tried the words of the Prophet and who knew for himself that in the Light was the best place to live, tried to tell his friends that in order to honor the Prophet they must not merely call him their Lord and Leader but take him at his word and move out into the Sunlight. And some listened and came out, at first with pain but then with unbelievable joy; and they would not again return under the Umbrellas to find the Sun. But others preferred the way of faith in the Umbrellas and heeded not his words. Instead they went on praising the Prophet of the Sun while living under the Umbrellas. "After all," they said, "We know that we have been freed from the darkness of the House of Legality." And they went on so believing.

Evangelism today must be directed largely to Christians. Most of us work chiefly among those who confess Christ and belong to the Church. Yet, confessing and belonging, we live under Umbrellas. Our faith is in Umbrellas. We trust generally in the historic Jesus, in the Bible and in the Church, but have no vital, personal, all-absorbing life with God Himself. We pray "through Jesus Christ our Lord," but we seldom get through! We do not personally get through to God. God Himself is a stranger to us, although God is Himself the God of all comforts, before, beyond and through all things. At the heart of the universe and at the heart of our lives, therefore, is no irrepressible joy; the Gospel for us is all too often more duty than gladness. It is more believed in than believed. It is more accepted than understood; it is more learned and imbibed than experienced at first hand.

To reach such religious people was the task of Jesus; it was the task of St. Francis; the task of Luther; of Wesley. To reach such religious people, called "Christians," is the task awaiting the prophet or prophets today.

But how can they, when they come, really reach the people? Prophetic spirits have usually been impatient with established religion and have generally been in trouble with it. Such a troublous state has absorbed much of their time and thinking and has often warped their attitudes.

How can we remove Umbrellas and still be so concerned with the people under them, loving them without reservation, that we ourselves do not become warped by a fight with them? Christianity has become largely a prey to Scribism and Pharisaism. Traditionalistic orthodoxy has to be challenged, fought and slain. Umbrellas must be folded to let in the Sun. The good news of God's availability to each seeker beyond his every expectation must be proclaimed and practiced. Ours it is to be heralds of the glorious message of Christian liberty in Christ and of the whole heart of God for the world. Is it possible, however, to destroy hindrances to the Gospel without losing our positive constructive zeal for Christ?

Our problem is this: how can we go from idolatry to Incarnation without losing the worshipers in the process? How can we release the immeasurable power of God in Christ apart from the mythology which hides Him from the world? How can we go from traditionalistic Christian orthodoxy to the Church of the Living God without becoming a new denomination? Or if we are ready to pass into a new name and era how can we make effectively central to truth and life what Jesus was and taught? How can we develop the implications of the Word made flesh without alienating those who mean, too, to worship the same God? How can we let the original Incarnation be still original today—and originating? How can God

become central without an antichristian movement or one
that neglects Christ as eternal truth and reality? How, in
other words, can we carry on an effective evangelism to Christians? How also can we make this determined fight against
Christian idolatry without losing our full-fashioned love of the
Incarnate Lord? Can we give up worshiping Christ after the
flesh without giving Him up as well?

God is more than a "Sun" that radiates power and gives
sustaining life to the world. God is a personal Spirit with a
free creative purpose. He acts in creation. He acts in history.
He acts in individual lives. He acts not only generally and
regularly but also specifically and occasionally. As a matter of
fact, in the long and large perspective, human life and history
must be seen mostly in terms of God's action, God's initiative.
This is particularly true on the level of human redemption.
He acts particularly in a select way in special providence
through those who are open to His purpose. He sees when
preparation is ready, when time is full, and calls His messengers
accordingly by special callings, empowerings and leadings.

Therefore, the coming of the Word was basically the work
of God. It was, in fact, God's own coming into history. Incarnation involves the self-entrance of God Himself. This is His
main purpose with creation and with history: to fulfill the
life of man by His own living in and through them. For this
reason the Incarnation of God's love in Jesus must be viewed
not primarily as Jesus' response, but first of all as God's entering human history in a new and radical way. The main dimension of God's love taking on human form, expressing Himself
in human history, is His own eternal purpose to send His
own Son in the fullness of time. Time's becoming full is to

be understood as God's calling and sustaining the people of Israel, the chosen race. This preliminary enactment of God's purpose within a given community was the preparation which was needed in order for the fullness of time to draw nigh.

In one way such choice of a people by God may seem arbitrary and lacking in universal concern; but God acts personally in the rough and concrete choices of history and not merely naturalistically or deistically through the regular routes of nature or the general processes of history. The choice is for all people ultimately; and those who are chosen are usually chosen to suffer, to share God's redemptive activity. This is a privilege only to those who are ready by background and spirit for such a task. Nor is the choice predestinarian and particularistic in the sense that no human response in real freedom is involved. The secondary human response is required. God does not force fellowship. He does not thrust love upon His children. Although history is particularistic and although God does take initiative in calling specific persons and people, the history of redemption is always conditional upon the kind of response which is given by the persons and the people.

This concept of God's historic activity must be supplemented by another concept—that of truth. The heart of truth is not a matter of things or of ideas but of a Person confronting persons. Therefore, all philosophical systems fall short of truth, except as they point to it; and no science can more than describe the outer garments of reality. We need both philosophy and science, but they can never take the place of the inner reality which is truth as encounter and truth as experienced reality. The living personal Spirit is the heart of truth. The more our spirits live with Him and in line with His purpose the more truth we know. The more we want to communicate truth the more we must be truth or point to *the enactment* of truth in other spirits. Love cannot be found in any formula, however brilliant and exact. Love can never be contained within any book, no matter how exhaustive. God is truth at its center. In Him alone we strike the inner heart of reality. Our whole being can never rest until it rests in Him as the truth, the way and the life.

Statements about God, therefore, are best expressed in persons who are in right relation to Him, who are God-possessed. The Spirit Himself must bear witness with our spirits that we are children of God. Our finite spirit can never know the depth of truth until the Infinite Spirit touches it with His light, assurance and sense of reality. This is the inner personal experience of God and the Gospel. The outward expression, communication or witness must be through the pointing to people who have the Spirit, or are "had" by the Spirit.

For this reason the Gospel is the truth as it is in Jesus. It is the story of Jesus' life, death and rising again. Here sacrificial love is lived, and becomes victorious. Here God is most fully revealed. Some scholars talk about the original *kerygma*, others of the need of myth. The truth is that God's presence must be pictured in persons and in concrete deeds more than in abstract meanings or philosophical formulations. Jesus, therefore, spoke truly about his being the truth and doing the truth. Truth at its innermost is more lived than spoken.

Since truth is at its heart personal and spiritual, to be received most fully, inwardly, through the Spirit; and since truth is expressed most fully, outwardly, in terms of a life filled by the Spirit, truth was never made more manifest than in Jesus of Nazareth. Thus quite naturally the historic Jesus has been continuously used as an Umbrella—as a substitute for God instead of His true representative. God was in Christ and we ought, therefore, no longer to know Jesus in a human way but to go through Christ our Lord to God. Faith should be through and through God-centered in doctrine and in life. The fact that God became conclusively incarnate in Jesus, that the eternal Person—who is ever the Word—became organically the dominant reality in the life of Jesus, means that God became truly self-revealed and miraculously effective in human history. We know no other God than He who came in Jesus, the God who is eternal *Agape*, the New Testament kind of Love.

That God became incarnate does not mean, however, that the human Jesus is God or that his human personality pre-existed from all eternity. *Such is the nature of the grand myth which at its heart is idolatry.* Nor does it mean that the human Jesus does not always belong with us, a creature among creatures. On this point orthodoxy is heretical. Here traditionalistic Christianity is idolatrous. The fact that historically we came to know God as *Agape* conclusively through this God-thrust into history in Jesus—so that he mediates our knowledge of God and the effective working of God in human salvation—should be a source of inexpressible gratitude to God and to Jesus himself. But it does not allow us to deify the creature, before or after his earthly life. God the eternal has here shown His heart and reached down His strong arm to save. This is now our God, our Father, our Savior. God has opened the heavenly gates of understanding and access. Our task is to believe and to enter.

If such theological distinctions as these, however, become our main interests, we have no right to talk about evangelism. But there can be no vital evangelism till the practical obstacle to a full and living faith in God is removed. What really hurts is the fact that Jesus, instead of being considered the first born among many brethren, has been made into a unique being; not as the first born, not as the historic particular who is irreversibly the channel of revelation and redemption, but as the inimitable, the only one possible. The glad news of the Gospel, on the very contrary, is that anyone who accepts the fullness of God in his own life can have the full relation of Jesus, of a child to the Father. God through His son calls sons. Whoever genuinely wills and believes shall be led by the Holy Spirit into all truth and have the same work, or even greater, because Jesus has lived and made the Father available in this new fullness. Traditional theology by severing Jesus from man has undermined the whole meaning of Jesus and made the Gospel—the true evangel—of little effect.

There is no question of human optimism, no question of native human goodness, no question of evolutionary progress. There is a question of whether or not God's Christ is genuinely also in us, if we will receive Him, to become born neither of flesh nor of the will of man but of God. There is no question of the genuineness of the Incarnation but of its fuller acceptance. The question is not whether Jesus founded the Church, and as such is its head and Lord, but whether he did so in the Holy Spirit, because he was Christ-filled; whether the heart of the Church is now the same Christ; whether the Church is truly a Christian community within the effective grace of God. The issue is not whether God did something final in Jesus or showed His heart in such manner that no other absolute can ever be genuinely revealed. The issue is whether that finality can now touch and transform our finitude. The concern is not to make the Gospel smaller; the concern is to make the Gospel more full and real. Our need today is to repent and believe the Gospel, the whole gamut of the glad news of the grace of God. "Behold, I bring you good tidings of great joy which shall be to all people. For unto you is born this day in the city of David a Saviour, which is Christ the Lord"—born not basically in Bethlehem or Nazareth, but born within a Spirit-filled life with whom we are all joint heirs.

Evangelism to the Christians must consequently be in the power of the Holy Spirit. When the Christian faith was most real, running with young but eager feet into the pagan world, the hero was the Holy Spirit. Umbrellas were at their minimum. We must not overlook the record of the acts of the apostles which reveals how God works among men with the Holy Spirit as the active guide, empowerer and guarantee. Jesus had gone away that the Spirit might come. He came with what power! The same Holy Spirit is now urgently inviting Himself into our hearts and our humanity. The same Holy Spirit is waiting to turn the world upside up. The same Holy Spirit yearns to make God real and all things right. The same Holy Spirit is the holy hope of all those who live in the Sun. What we need is the power of Pentecost. What we can have is the power of Pentecost. The deepest longings of the people of God should be for that same power of Pentecost. Only as we wait together in prayer for the power from on high shall there be a basic revolution in the lives of men and in the conditions of civilization. Péguy says that religion begins in mysticism and ends in politics. The coming of the Spirit to bring in the true Christian community will organically affect all dimensions of life.

The Holy Spirit is God personally present. He is wisdom beyond our keenest thought. He is communication beyond our most penetrating speech. He is power for conviction beyond our most saintly example. He Himself is our only adequate hope. Only as we learn to live in Him and by Him, learning to speak in and by Him, shall we reach those who are already vaccinated against Christianity and cannot now find its original power. Only as He frees the heart from within shall the whole self dare to submerge itself in the deep waters of God's mercy. Only as He speaks with authentic truth shall those who have long lisped Christian words dare to believe. God personally present, God vitally anointing, God now fulfilling in human hearts and history His own purpose in Christ—that is the Holy Spirit, the personal Agent, the personal Director, the Captain in command. When He comes, conscience clicks with conviction and the mind is satisfied with truth.

Apart from Him Christians dare not lower their Umbrellas. Unless He is real they must shield themselves within orthodoxy. Without His holding on to them they must hold on to their man-made doctrines. These doctrines point to truth and came out of experience. But they are not truth and do not constitute experience. They are substitutes which hinder the Holy Spirit. Live, vital, verdant faith, ever shooting up in new growth, is lacking to jaded Christianity. Inexpressible and irrepressible love and faith fail nominal religionists.

The words of firsthand religion strike with the power of thunderbolts and are yet as tender as spring buds. They are as hard as rock and as pliable as mountain moss. They are both real and relevant. They are right and ready. But the words of religion at second hand weary. The most pious terms sound slippery, empty, nauseous to the honest seeker. Doctrine per se represents the realm of the mysterious unreal which is supposed to be believed, but which neither makes sense nor gives inner freedom. Only the Holy Spirit can give the click of conviction and wash out the grimy, oily words of orthodoxy. Only the Holy Spirit can release the conviction of reality that gives creative content to religious vocabulary.

He will not, however, force His way. He comes only in response to our acceptance. He woos and waits. His is the power to make all things new. His is the power to make real worship, witness and work. But we must answer to Him in faith. We must let Him into our lives. Faith in Him is the way of evangelism to the Christians. Faith in Him is the correction of orthodoxy. Faith in Him is the power for personal renewal. Faith in Him is the secret of the transformation of life and the Christian community. Whether we continue to use the glorious name "Christian" and have a radically remade Church or whether there shall be founded the wider and more intensive Church of the Living God depends completely on whether or not traditionalistic Christianity continues to worship its doctrinal development or is willing to start afresh at the foot of the Cross, God's complete self-giving answered by man's self-giving unto death.

Unless the providence of God shows another way, the Christian Church has no significant future till it puts away traditionalistic orthodoxy to let the light of God's love shine free and full for a world in need. Will the Church continue to dance around its golden calf of idolatry or will it be willing to humble itself before the eternal presence of God in Incarnation? Faith in the Incarnate God is now available to every humble and honest seeker—that is the good news of the Age of the Spirit, the true evangel to a world dying because it is hid from the Light.

Yet faith is impossible without prayer. Prayer is personal

communication with God. Prayer is man's real relation to God in the Spirit. Prayer is fellowship within the family. Prayer is living in, with and for God. Our faith must be born by the Holy Spirit, but nourished and sustained by prayer, as we keep opening our lives to the Holy Spirit. If nominal Christianity is to be awakened, born again, become a new creaturehood in Christ, such a transformation will depend upon the commitment to prayer in the Holy Spirit on the part of those who now belong to the quickened community of the Living God. Such prayer must be for God's total will through our whole lives for the entire world. It requires total honesty of dedication, total commitment to the Church of God's love, total stewardship of time, money and abilities. Such prayer can grow and be sustained only within the power of the Holy Spirit. Such prayer can be practiced only within whole-lived acceptance of faith. Such prayer, stimulating and freeing the mind to creative and critical study, releasing the springs of healing, energizing appropriate and consistent Christian action, is the prerequisite for the coming of the great age of evangelism to the Christians, when the dry bones will rise and walk; will work and sing.

Such evangelism to the Christians and such sustaining of the Church of the Living God requires that each confessor of the faith spend regular periods of time in the closed closet. Personal prayer with a Christian pattern and Pentecostal power must be practiced much more than daily. Prayer without ceasing must become more than a Biblical phrase or a pious injunction. The Christian community must train each member carefully, patiently in the practice of prayer; happily there is a growing literature available to all. Further, through months and years of perseverance, every person must be taught of the work of the Holy Spirit; here most of the books are yet to be written. But as God becomes real to more and more persons and the community becomes genuinely Christian, the Holy Spirit will add the daily testimony of those nominal Christians who are being saved to the community of the Living God.

Family prayers will also be part of the Church's life. The Church of the Living God cannot have families in which the faith is not alive. Children are prevented from believing by parents whose religion is mostly secondhand. Churchgoing easily takes the place of personal and family worship. Attendance at Church is supposed to satisfy the spiritual needs of life. But where God is real there is genuine, personal faith within the family. Therefore, the Church must insist that primary training in faith take place at home. Each mother and father must pray personally to be able to mediate reality through the family altar. Family prayers should never be allowed to become a duty and a routine. When family prayers lag, the power of Christian living is lost. Because of lukewarm faith family worship becomes dull and unreal. For those who belong to the Church of the Living God worshiping in the Holy Spirit, faith flowers naturally into the reality of family devotions. Family living and giving, family working and playing, family suffering and rejoicing—all are touched, transformed and hallowed by being in the sight of God.

Not only do members of the Church of the Living God seek to pray as families, but also the families come together corporately for prayer. The Church teaches them how to pray and to this training adds practice for individuals and groups. More private chapels are needed, enough for one and all, where people can feel free to go during the whole week. Many will pray in the sanctuary itself. Needless to say the Church should always be open. The practice of prayer from any pew at any time should be as natural as any part of living. The central place of prayer would naturally encourage families or community groups to come to the house of God when they want to perform a special act of dedication, sacrifice or commitment. There should be prayer groups within the community, meeting regularly for study and meditation. God's house should not only be called but *be* a house of prayer. Every service of corporate worship in the Spirit, however formal or liturgical, should also give place for personal prayer, a few moments of quiet in the living hush of the Eternal.

A Church based on prayer in the Living God cannot help becoming an evangel, the proclaimer of the Gospel through its very community and through the natural outreach of its members. What has been sketched here is actually Church evangelism as the very structure and function of worship. Such an evangelical community must be energized by prayer for the coming of His Kingdom everywhere—a worship answered by the Holy Spirit in power—through witness and soul-winning.

This community should also by its very organization bear witness to freedom and faithfulness in fellowship. Its way of functioning should enact the Gospel of the grace of God. Lack of structure is no sign of freedom but, rather, of confusion and inefficiency. An authoritarian organization, on the other hand, hardly witnesses even to order. Order cannot for long be organized into efficiency without that genuine freedom which makes for personal accountability and initiative. The Church of the Living God should be so patterned that order exists from the central executive function to local life, but this order would express freedom and seek to facilitate it.

This statement may be a good theory of organization, but how can it be practically implemented? All decisions of general importance ought to be decided by the chosen officials representing the Church as a whole; all matters of dominantly local importance should be locally determined. In each case responsibly delegated authority is needed. But the authority should always be subject to the natural and uncomplicated testing of both general and local groups. There should be definitely responsible study groups, generally and locally, and information and guidance should readily be channeled from one to another. In voting, all members should participate with equal voting weight, using the secret ballot, the closed closet before God. Initiative for general or local action should be open from the local to the general and from the the general to the local, but the power of decision should always reside with the general for the general and the local for the local.

No decisions should ever be finally reached until thorough study had made clear the several implications and involvements of any issue, in the light of the faith, of the present actual situation and in the light of probable results. In addition to these definitely binding rules for freedom in fellowship, there should be a rule that all matters for decision, generally and locally, should be made the object of special prayers by all relevantly selected members personally in the closed closet; by the families at their devotional hour, and followed, as far as practical, by family discussion; and by the Church as a unit, whether locally or generally. Special groups might also be chosen under certain circumstances to pray through any bothersome issue. Always full reliance should be made on the guidance of the Holy Spirit, but never in such a way as to deprive individuals or the community from responsibility under God and from the chance of growing in grace through common struggle with common problems.

The conditions for membership in the community should be total commitment to the will of God by His grace, total commitment to the Church of the Living God, and total concern for the world. Only those born from above, those integrated anew around the will of God for the world, can make such commitments or live such concern. God's will should be defined as total love for the world, not as a means which makes the world central but as His very nature which makes God central. Neither an individual nor a world community can ever fulfill its real nature and destiny apart from the acceptance of God's will as central. The commitment should be by God's grace and according to the fullest possible understanding of His nature.

No entrance requirement will bar admittance to this open community of learning and confession, other than this original and repeated commitment as evidenced by faith and works. The commitment to the Church should be not primarily to an institution but to the community as a fellowship of faith. While the Church must not become an Umbrella, the fellowship does need a living organization as fully as possible expressive of its faith. No directive as to worship, sacrament, ordinance or polity may ever become ultimate and a cause for division. Forms of worship, symbols and details of organization should aim to satisfy general unity and also all needed difference. They should all be serious matters to be studied, discussed and prayed about, but never matters of salvation to disrupt or divide the community.

The unchanging faithfulness of God for all people is the major affirmation of the Church of the Living God. This is the heart of its Gospel and evangelism. This is the love which Jesus enacted and taught. This is the reality of the Holy Spirit. This is the guarantee of the gift of grace. This is, incidentally, the kind of Church for which Abraham Lincoln looked in vain. The Church of the Living God is the community of the God who is both infinitely high and lifted up and yet lives in holy love in and with His people. This is the Church of transcendence and Incarnation. The Church of the Living God is the Church for one world and for all worlds. As open as truth, it is also as real as the Father's presence in the closet, in the midst of two or three or in the community as a whole. Thus its very form is a witness to, and an expression of, the Gospel; it is an evangel to all those who have long been weary and discouraged with traditionalistic Christianity.

The Christian community is ever intensive and effective. Therefore property, insofar as it comes under the jurisdiction of the Church of the Universal God, must be considered common for each and all under God. Whatever property be delegated to individual or group responsibility is for the development of freedom and initiative in fellowship. Community control under God cannot, therefore, stifle individual responsibility in property matters. Basically property is God's good gift for stewardship by the community, the family and the individual, and the attitudes and actions of the Church of the Living God must witness to this fact.

As far as the Church of the Living God has influence or power in the realm of property, it should seek to place the means of production in the hands of the community but with such individual rewards and responsibilities of consumer's goods as develop personality. Social incentives will always be thwarted unless the organization of property be conducive to community integration. Truly to live the Gospel of the grace of God is to prepare in life and legislation both the incentives and the structures which will make property the servant of the people. Too long we have subordinated people, in effect, to property. The Marxists wrongly believe that property relations need to be changed by revolution before the right social incentives can emerge. The Church of the Living God knows, however, that right relations to God *in attitude and action, in function and organization*, alone will transform society, leading toward freedom and faithfulness in fellowship, the Christian pattern for community in God.

The Church of the Universal God will develop such an inviolable community that for its members war becomes unthinkable. The early Christian Church refused totalitarianism and war, without repudiating civil authority. What rare wisdom born from above! The enactment of God's universal community in the fullness of time is more important for social improvement than any other action. God has created nature and guides history as a whole. He works in them in accordance with the rules of their natures; accordingly loyalty and sacrifice on man's common level of insight and commitment are to be honored. Ours is not to judge the loyalties of honorable people tangling with tough political problems.

But confessing Christians should live in a new age of human history, an age where the true community from heaven has been revealed through Jesus Christ. Those who know the reality of the experience of the new age within the love of God know as obviously as light is not dark that universal community and war are basically contradictory; and that their own total loyalty to God's will coincides with the inviolable community in Christ. Those who are new creatures within the Gospel of the grace of God do not argue about war; nor do they try simply to persuade the people who are not yet on this level of life to give up war. They witness, rather, to the reality within the love of God of the new community of the new age, within which war is no longer a question. The Church of the one God and the one world transcends redemptively such conflicts as war among its own groups. Such transcendence is ever for the world as a whole, the winning witness to the kind of community to which all men are called by the grace of God.

Within the community of the Living God, furthermore, race is no barrier. Segregation is the sign and seal of sin. To be sure, cultural pluralism is good. People who are alike want and need to be together. The natural patterns of life are built on this principle. But such differentiation based on desire is far different from segregation based on compulsion. All God's children are welcome within the warmth of the Church of the Living God. The witness of this community must be genuine love within, including all men and the constant, fervent endeavor to live so wisely and so well that communications are opened everywhere. Then the spirit is created, within the grace of God, which increasingly dissolves the emotional blocks which make rational dealing with problems of color well-nigh impossible. Christ requires the kind of community where segregation is the sign and seal of sin, but wherein the Holy Spirit is the guarantee of the gift of God's grace to forgive the sin and to restore the broken relation. Love will also serve its community realistically in terms of economic, social and political opportunities.

Very likely the Christian community that is to come will produce adequate and attractive newspapers, periodicals, radio

and television programs and motion pictures. When we pray
"Lead us not into temptation," we must mean it enough to
do away with the common and constant temptations of a
degenerate civilization. If we allow our children to be surrounded by evil influences, have we the right to use the Lord's
Prayer? Society as a whole may not become Christianized, certainly not unless it undergoes a spiritual transmutation of
hitherto unguessed proportions. But the Christian community
can provide the kind of social environment which facilitates,
not destroys, Christian behavior patterns.

All failures of fellowship that arise, such as divorce and
breach of the civil law in general, should be increasingly
settled within the confines and spirit of the Church of the
Living God. To the extent the fellowship is real and effective
the community will help prevent such failures. In China the
villagers lived long and well without police. Failures were han-
dled by family conclaves. In India the caste system could deal
effectively with problems of discipline. Arab countries have
generally been honest and true to their pledged word and the
sacred meal of friendship.

Beset by crimes within and wars without, the nominally
Christian nations bear witness to the spiritual poverty of their
peoples. The Church of the Living God must become such
an intensive and effective community in the power of the
Holy Spirit, worship, faith and prayer that radical changes take
place in all social, civic and legal patterns. Discipline must
be unsentimental, austere and effective, precisely because guilt
can be forgiven and the fellowship restored. But the consequences of sin must be borne within the self-offerings of
genuine repentance. Such repentance will always have political
as well as social consequences. Where there is no transforma-

tion of actual social patterns there is also no vital spiritual power.

Where there is no repentance there must, of course, be exclusion, not for the sake of the community primarily, but first and foremost for the sake of the unrepentant. All severing of relations should also be carried out so as to offer genuine love to the one excluded and to promise full restoration whenever he is ready to accept the basis of God's inclusive and responsibly concerned Love. On occasion the community may itself assume consequences of individual wrongdoing so redemptively that where there is genuine repentance, external discipline will become a secondary matter. No repentance can be genuine, however, that does not put right what can be put right. Possibly, too, even beyond these considerations, the patterns of the community may develop flexibilities within its vital relation to God which may not be judged externally, but be subject solely to the wisdom of the community of the new age. In any case, however austere the discipline, it must be within the spirit of discipleship, the inclusive love of God for all men. The first responsibility of the Church of the Living God to the world, moreover, is to be its own true self, the inviolable community in Christ. As such it is a community of acceptance and appreciation. The whole creation is good, from God, and to be accepted with thanksgiving and prayer. The disciplined life, personally and communally, is the life of total commitment to God, to the community, and with full concern for the world. Where such concern is genuine, there will be stewardship of time, ability and resources. They will be at the disposal of God, the community and the world. Such customs as smoking, drinking and personal adornment will not be put on the level of law, but will become questions as to how God's resources can best be used to glorify Him, to make the community real and to help the world.

Pleasure and play are part of the full life. For both, the community of appreciation and acceptance will be thankful and will include them fully within its being. But resolutely to be curbed are whatever pleasure and play that curtail the productive use of land to feed the world or that so abuse the body as to be either a personal problem or a social danger; curbed, not merely externally by prohibition and redirection, but by a frank facing of the facts and by a true dedication of life with its resources to God. As a revitalized civilization finds new methods of food and energy—solar, chemical, atomic, from the ocean, or what not—and as, increasingly, there are fewer hours spent in work, there will be more opportunity for play and pleasure as a part of creative living. The Church of the Living God will, therefore, be unsentimental in its dealing with personal habits within the perspective of general need, but also resolute in its rejection of moralism, refusing to judge people in terms of external habits and to act out of a guilt relation which feels pleasure and play to be wrong. In this natural and wholehearted acceptance and appreciation of life the Church of the Living God will be a living enactment of the Gospel of the grace of God. The community will find the power to overcome both self-indulgence and moralism.

Apart from being its own true self by the grace of God, the Church of the Living God will have three basic relations to the world. The first is a living witness to it in evangelism and missions. How this can be done I shall treat separately at length. The second is the giving of its substance to the needs of the world. Talk is cheap and words flow all too easily. The Church will witness through its giving, naturally, gladly, wisely and in all constructive areas. Increasingly it will give more to prevent than to cure trouble. It will give spontaneously when disaster strikes and it will give steadily and inconspicuously where there are areas of constant want. God gives because He loves. The Church of the Living God will be the Church also of the giving God. By its very nature it will overbrim and overflow. In modern civilization most giving will, however, have to be appropriated and distributed through effective impersonal agencies.

Then, third, the Church will participate responsibly in all areas of decision and duty. By its witness and its work the Church will help in the achievement of justice in the world as a whole. It will co-operate in forming legislation and in enforcing legislation. This it will do through its own delegated groups who study civic problems and report back on them to the community, general and local. This it will do through groups organized to guide legislation and who are in effective touch with the molding of general public opinion and specialized legislative opinion. This it will do through groups who devote their time to community responsibilities in the concrete outworking of legislation. This it will do through the creation of community morale. This it will do through the raising up and training of individual members who become technically competent in specialized areas. This it will do indirectly through the influence of its life on its members who vote and legislate.

The Church must be the salt of the earth, not theoretically, but in the midst of hard and unpleasant realities. The Church must be the light on the hill: on the hill first of all, its own true community, but also letting its light shine into the places of darkness. The more the Church becomes real, as a total way of living, the less need for courts, prisons and police; the less need for legislation and enforcement of criminal laws.

The world stands on the brink of possible disaster. Even more it stands on the brink of a new and better day. This day it can enter insofar as we accept the Gospel of God's will for the world, in the Holy Spirit, in faith and in prayer. This is possible through the community of the new age. No slightly improved Christian Church will do. It must be a basically re-directed and dominantly motivated community of God's love which is both present and powerful in the world. Then all of our resources and all of our time will be utilized to realize the freedom and faithfulness of fellowship which is God's eternal purpose for the world. Then a new joy, freedom and reality will make all of us free souls within the will of God. This is our evangelism to the Christians!

The Sun and the Umbrella
Ferre

Name

Date
Taken

Date
Returned

V

Light for Jews

Those who now were in the Light, however, could not forbear to go everywhere to tell about that Light. Not only did they return to those who worshiped the Sun under Umbrellas while averring to live fully in the Light, but they also went into the House of Legality to share their good news with the people there, and they ventured into all the earth, into houses of strange religions. . . .

Evangelism to the Jews has been a problem to Christianity. From one point of view Christianity is Judaism universalized. It took over the Jewish faith in a personal God who dealt personally with prophets, people and history. Christianity, to a large extent, has had the Jewish view of time and of history as created and governed by the eternal Spirit. Judaism had a messianic sense of being called by God for a special and fulfilling mission, which became part and parcel of the Christian faith. Church life sprang out of the synagogue.

A high sense of righteousness, or moral accountability to God, was also a Jewish heritage. The Jewish stress on the goodness of creation and man's ability to do that which God commands, however, has had a mixed history, concealed behind the Christian doctrine of the sinfulness of man and his redemption in Christ. Not that Judaism was not a religion of redemption! On the contrary, this element has always been a strong force in Jewish piety. The Christian approach, however, sharpened the sense of sin, the impotence of man and the corruption of nature. In its doctrine of redemption it centralized the Temple at the expense of the synagogue, community worship and living as the way of God.

This sharpened sense of sin drew largely on pagan sources, as my colleague George Mayhew maintains, rather than Jewish, and Judaism offers a corrective to the Christian teaching. On the other hand, a heightened view of God's universal love in Christ lit up man's sin more brightly. Therefore, the Christian faith needed more than an intensified stress on grace to match the pagan view of sin to which it became subject. The Christian faith needed a doctrine of grace strong enough to meet its own keener burden of guilt.

Basically Christianity can be considered as the universalization of Judaism. As it spread out into the pagan world it absorbed pagan elements. From one point of view, therefore, it is a corrupt Judaism which needs the witness of the original Jewish faith, the Judaism both within and outside the Church. Those who look at the relation of Christianity to Judaism in this way naturally feel no need for evangelism to the Jews. Prominent Christian thinkers are convinced that Judaism needs to retain its identity in order to constitute for the Christian Church a conscience against paganism.

Fundamentalists take the other point of view. The Jews must accept the Savior whom they have denied. They must open their eyes to their own Scriptures to find their own prophecies concerning Jesus. One day they are to return to Jerusalem and there will be a large-scale conversion of the Jews to Christ. That day may even now be on the verge of being fulfilled. Their years of suffering, however, are the result of their crucifixion of Jesus and of their cry for his blood to come upon them and upon their children. The fundamentalists, therefore, carry on a tract movement, pleading with the Jews, in effect, to become fundamentalists, thereby surrendering entirely their specific Jewish heritage. It can hardly be said that a Jew by becoming Christian ever gives up his whole Jewish history, but he certainly does accept one kind of history for another.

Neither of these approaches seems adequate to truth or to actual life. The Jews themselves vary in their response to the Christian appeal. To the Orthodox Jew Christianity is blasphemy. God is one, eternal and holy. To say that a man was God is to offend incalculably the eternal God, who is ever God and not man. Christianity is idolatry. Some of it has been guilty of a long history of unspeakable persecution of the Jewish people. All talk of Christianity's being universal love is sharply contradicted by the history of the Christian people in their actual relation to the Jews. It has been a history of exploitation, persecution and a refusal to understand their deep devotion and piety. To be sure, many individual Christians and many Christian groups have been personally kind and helpful, but this is because they have lost the fanatical in-group zeal which Christianity inspires.

Even today anti-Semitism has taken a terrible toll, is rampant in Christian communities and is ever a phenomenon which can break out like a plague whenever there are economic,

political or social frustrations. The Jews are still the scapegoats
of the Christians, even so lacking the high redemptive mission
of the scapegoat. Most of those within this meaning and mood
see little real relation between Christianity and Judaism and
have no genuine hope of finding a common religion which will
be fully true and workable for both. With regard to their own
faith, too, they take a narrow, intensive point of view. The
restricted interpretation of Judaism deals with God's messianic
promises to His chosen people, hallowed be His name, and it
is no business of Judaism to step beyond the boundaries of
God's own choice and guidance. Judaism is *Torah*, a living
way within the Law of Moses for the chosen people. To look
beyond this loyalty is to court the disasters of idolatry and
contamination against which all the great prophets of Israel
constantly fought.

The liberal Jew, be he denominationally Reformed or not,
has discarded traditionalistic Judaism. He is no fundamentalist.
He does not "believe" the Bible in a naïve or literal way. He
has given up the legalistic traditions of his people, in general,
and frequently does not feel bound even by the dietary laws.
He does not expect an earthly messiah. Nevertheless, Judaism
for him is a cultural continuity which he accepts. Perhaps he
does not attend the synagogue. He may not even believe in
God. But he is conscious of being a Jew and appreciates his
Jewish heritage. He does not believe in the political promises
of God for the Jews to recover Palestine but he may rejoice
in Zionism in the same way that other nationalities feel the
call upon them of their own distinctiveness. These Jews are
not readily won by fundamentalist tracts or sermons. They
have gone through the critical stage of religious thinking and
cannot except by default return to any precritical religion.

Other Jews have to a large extent universalized their religion, while recognizing the need and legitimacy of cultural distinctiveness. Some of them have made the love of God central. Certainly the stress on "the faithful love" of God is very strong in the Old Testament and may well be considered its highest pinnacle of revelation. These Jews have gone on through a process similar to the one which Jesus went through and have made Judaism the carrier of the universal love of God for the world. They, therefore, reject political Zionism as false nationalism; they accept residence in any land, appreciating its cultural heritage in a broad co-operative manner. Can there be any kind of evangelism to these Jews or are they already members in fact of the universal community of the Living God?

The answer to this question can be indicated only in broad, general terms. The Christian who looks at Christianity as a universalizing of Judaism with some historic particularity added, pagan or otherwise, stands at one extreme; the tractarian fundamentalist who uses Bible prophecies to understand the history of the Jews since the death of Jesus stands at the other. The orthodox messianic Jew who feels self-sufficient within Judaism as the revelation to the chosen people stands at one extreme. The liberal Jew who accepts Judaism as mostly a cultural heritage and universalizes the nature and message of Judaism as the religion of the Living God—hallowed be His name—for the world, stands at the other extreme. In between are numerous shades of opinion, attitudes and practices.

An evangelism to the Jews must first consider these differing views of Christianity and Judaism. In no way do I see a possible evangelism within the dimension of an authoritarian orthodoxy, Christian or Jewish. All externalistic revelations close the gates to understanding and to communication. At the same time, all loose liberal analyses which fail to take absolute truth seriously fail to satisfy. Theology cannot be by-passed. It must be the highroad to truth, to the truth which unites men within the freedom of reality.

Evangelism to the Jews must be based on three appeals: that of God, of Christ and of culture. Christians and Jews should worship the same God, the God of universal love. Only that truth can make any of us free. God *is Agape*, the totally out-going concern for all men, sovereign and all-wise, holy and all-righteous. His is the Love which includes all, even though most persons can for a very long time shut themselves off from Him, not entirely because of their ignorance but also because of a combination of self-will and self-seeking which hides from them the light which they could have if they would.

The objection will be made that this God the Jews neither know nor worship and that this proposal, therefore, amounts to sheer Christian imperialism. Some scholars affirm that the Old Testament never went beyond election-love and covenant-love, and that therefore Judaism has suffocated its doctrine of love within an ethnic parochialism, continuing in a state of arrested development. To this objection two replies must be made. The first is that the Old Testament has a larger view of God—for instance Job, Ruth and Second Isaiah, or even in the best impulses, for that matter, of passages like Leviticus 19. While the doctrine of *Agape* may never have become explicit in Judaism, it throbs behind and within the best and highest of Old Testament religion. The understanding of God grows in the Old Testament and the eternal God of *Agape* stands within the shadow of the finest flowering of Old Testament faith.

The second observation is that we have no right to equate

Judaism with the religion of the Old Testament. It has its own living growth through saints and seers. Jesus stood within this growth and belongs to Judaism as its natural fulfillment. Love to God and men was explicitly commanded and continually developed throughout Jewish history both before and after Jesus. Whether or not modern Jewish thinkers have learned from Jesus, they have also learned from and developed their own tradition, and have gone far "beyond the measure" of election-love.

A third and just observation can be added, namely, that this God of *Agape* has not been uniformly understood or accepted within Christianity. Both in New Testament times and later, limitations and contradictions exist. Much in traditionalistic theology has, in fact, denied rather thoroughly that God is *Agape* and the actual history of Christianity has convincingly denied this claim in the lives of its own community, particularly with reference to its relation to the Jews. Both Jews and Christians, therefore, may come together from afar into their own normative faith as fulfilled within the conclusive and universal love of God.

There can be no other foundation on which Christians and Jews can get together with full satisfaction. Its truth alone will win the final day. In the long last we can do everything for it and nothing against it. Therefore, the approach to both Christians and Jews must be on the level of truth, in method and in attitude. Naturally a faith stance can never be conclusively demonstrated. It cannot be proved like an empirical investigation or a mathematical problem, but it can be confirmed both in critical and creative thought and it must be self-authenticating in life. This complete concern for all men, God's *Agape*, to bestow upon them personally and as groups the fullest possible freedom and the best chance for creative development and expression, when answered by responsible and loyal freedom on the part of the persons and the group, is the most seminal clue to the deepest and most inclusive interpretation of experience and reality. This concern constitutes the locus of solution for our individual and social practical problems. The more we walk in the way of this truth, the more the actual goal is proved in experience to be, not only theoretical, but living truth.

God as *Agape* will satisfy the mind that reaches out for the most adequate perspective of interpretation and will satisfy the faith that is committed to the fullest possible acceptance of all that is good and to the ultimate transformation of all that is evil. This great God of the universes and this near God of the human heart alone can fulfill the requirements of faith and reason in their mutual interactions whether in the study or in the shop. This Creative Love is the truth of religion which is fully based on reality. Christians and Jews alike should, therefore, humbly and victoriously worship the Living God and become one within His community of love, that unsentimental, austere, majestic love within which we can become most fully and intimately our true and social selves.

The actual stumbling block, however, is Christ. Jesus divides Christians from Jews. Some say that this must be so until the Jews yield and accept Christ. Others hold this stumbling block to be a false offense which could be removed if Christians would only repent of their idolatry. The fact is, however, that Jesus is both a false and a true offense to the Jews. Christianity is more than Judaism universalized and different from it. It is not enough to say: "We Christians will give up our false particularism of paganism while you Jews give up your false particularity of ethnocentricity; whereupon both of us will find a common faith within the universal love of God." The reason that such a position fails is that Christianity is unalterably the religion of the Incarnation.

Precisely what does this fact involve for our evangelism to the Jews? It means a new understanding of God as Love with reference to the community of the Living God. The Jews generally conceived of God as completely transcendent to the world which He had made. He created man, sustained him, even spoke to him, but He was never in man, nor in the world. The Incarnation on this basis would have to be not only something miraculously external, an arbitrary thrust into human history, but also something offensive, a confounding of categories. The All-Holy remains ever high and lifted up; He never becomes man. For any man to make the claim that he literally is the son of God, that God is in him personally, is thus blasphemy. The Jews had a right to reject Jesus on the basis of their own holiest faith and no one should blame them for being horrified at his teachings. His subversive activities of breaking the Sabbath and the traditions were bad enough, but his claims concerning his own person were such that when he confessed them before their highest tribunal they needed in truth no other evidence of his guilt.

It was against the background of this kind of transcendent thinking that most Christian theology was formulated. Therefore, the person of the Christ became an insuperable barrier—or so it seemed to honest and earnest Jewish thinkers —to the worship of the one true God of Israel. This barrier was reinforced by theories of atonement and resurrection which further aggravated the difference between the Way and orthodox Judaism. Historically the discrediting of the

Jewish Law as necessary to right relation with God was also a main cause of separation. As Jesus, furthermore became more and more a substitute for God both in theology and in common devotion, the Jews became more and more horrified. Idolatry paraded nearly naked before their very eyes. Even in our day a strong movement in Christian theology is asserting the Godhood of Jesus within this context of transcendence. Certainly we cannot expect the thoughtful and devoted Jews to accept such evangelism; for it is not true.

Oppositely some have advocated immanence as a solution. Some of this stress has actually gone so far as to claim that God is only an aspect of process. Supernaturalism has been repudiated. Jesus, in this view, insofar as he is even accepted as the criterion of Christianity, is history's most high. He is potential man actualized. He is man normalized. He is our own inner true selves. There are various shades of meaning and various degrees to which reality is reduced to process, but in all cases where immanence is the uppermost, man's relation to God is characterized by continuity rather than discontinuity. Man is son of God by the native dignity of his soul which needs only to be developed or unfolded. Sin and redemption have naturally no pivotal places in such thinking.

Both transcendence and immanence must be rejected as basic ways of approaching the relation of man to God, and of Jesus to all men. The Christian criterion is, rather, Incarnation. From this point of view God is Creator, Sustainer, Judge, Redeemer and Fulfiller, and as such He is definitely and determiningly not the world. He is before, above and beyond all created being and processes. Even as Father and Friend of the human family He is not merely One among many, but the One upon whom all else depends. God the uncreated, the self-existent, the eternal is never created man nor is He material. God is God and not man; God is God and not the world—and that to all eternity. But in both these instances He who is qualitatively different from man and the world forever is nevertheless present both with and in His family and His creation.

God is not fully defined apart from the Love which is creative Being. Without creating, God would not be the God He eternally is in His own nature. Nor is this creation a by-product ruled by an absentee Landlord. God is with His creation, whether passively or personally, from moment to moment. Creation has a certain independence in order that it may perform its own work, but nature cannot be defined and understood apart from God. Nor can man in the full meaning of his nature and destiny be understood apart from God. God cohabits man's life through His generally sustaining and controlling power on the level of His body; He cohabits man's life as the individuating drive on the level of his created spirit; and He intends to cohabit man's life in full fellowship on the level of the Holy Spirit. Before Jesus came, God had worked mightily in the history of a certain people and a certain line of prophets, in particular, to prepare for the understanding and acceptance of His own Self as the Holy Spirit.

The fullness of time was no messianic, predestinarian particularity of history. It was an actual occurrence in the history of human freedom where God's total self-giving was answered by man's self-giving to Him and to the world. In Jesus history received its center because Reality was recognized and received. God's work was no predestined imposition, some external manipulation of man's history whereby a certain line of salvation was readied and fulfilled. It was, rather, His wondrous sovereign coworking with human freedom. God's self-giving, God's initiative, God's purpose were central to the Incarnation, completing conclusively the kind of relation which He eternally purposes for the world. None the less—even though God in Christ became actually the center of human history in Jesus—Jesus was, through and through, a human being, even as you and I. Both the divine and the human are organically fulfilled in this union of God-man which Jesus originated and exemplified. Not only was the combination organically fulfilled in him, but also it revealed God's eternal intention of the qualitatively different in Godhood and the qualitatively different in manhood. God's purpose and man's nature were organically fulfilled within a truly real person. The same purpose God intends to fulfill in all human beings. Until man so receives God, God's purpose is thwarted and man remains unfulfilled. Incarnation is thus the center of God's nature and of man's destiny.

Jews have been falsely offended by a doctrine of Christ which is idolatry and which deifies the human. God is one and selfsame forever. Jesus never was or became God. Although his human personality became fulfilled by his divine in such a way that he symbolically ascended to the right hand of God, and although the divine and human organically constitute one person, nevertheless, the divine as uncreate always remains divine whereas the human as created always remains human. Jesus came to be in time and remains forever on the human side of reality. But the essential fact about him is not his teaching nor his life but his incarnating of God. He was far more than a great teacher; he was far more than the greatest of the prophets. He was the first in the Kingdom, the founder of the new community, the bringer of the new age. He was the initiator of the new covenant based on better promises and reality. What matters is not that he may have been history's most high or that his teachings are unsurpassed, but that God in him became flesh; history was fulfilled by God's actual presence, power and promise. In Jesus we find savingly, in truth, both God's nature and that of the world in which we live, the latter being through this union *actually* illumined and judged, and *potentially* illumined and saved.

God was thus organically present in Jesus, fulfilling His purpose and our destiny. Here is revelation. Here is Incarnation. Here is power for the forgiveness of sin and the making of the new community in Christ. Christ is God's love come to earth. He is the Logos, the Word. This Christ, God's outgoing love, created, sustained and directed the world before Jesus; this Christ illumined every person who came into the world before him; and this Christ upheld the universes and dwelt in men while Jesus walked on earth. Christ must very definitely and particularly be identified with Jesus; but He must never be equated with him. Christ is conclusively God in Jesus for the world, but not exclusively. He came to His own and to all who will receive Him He gives power to become sons of God who are born not of flesh nor of the will of the flesh but of God. The destiny of our human personalities is to be fulfilled by the divine; Christ in us is the hope of glory.

Chronologically and organically Jesus mediates our knowledge of God. We know no other God than Him who came in Jesus. Actually, too, God's redemptive power became released both through a new understanding of God and through a new relation to Him. This relation was a new possibility and power of God within human history to judge, to forgive and to effect community. But as God was in Jesus so He should be in us also and we should all walk even as he walked. The Holy Spirit is He who alone makes us whole, fulfills our natures, fulfills our time organically by His eternity. Jesus was historically but not eternally unique. His humanity mediates historically the Incarnation. His divinity lights, judges and saves our own humanity.

If he was a "sport of evolution," as such he starts a new line, a new community, a new age, a new history. Jesus was the firstborn and the forerunner, summarizing, cleansing, clarifying and fulfilling Judaism and anticipating the Church of the Living God. God craves to be in us all exactly what He was and is in Jesus. The nature of man cannot be understood or fulfilled except through Incarnation. Transcendence is not miraculously bridged, immanence is not naturally fulfilled. But Incarnation, the new reality of God as He is in human history and personal life, judging and fulfilling man's old age by the power and reality of the new age in Christ, is the deepest relation of God to man. Sin is serious and forgiveness is necessary, but deeper and greater is the eternal purpose for fellowship in Christ which is man's proper and potential nature. Christ came in Jesus. Christ comes now to us. This is the Gospel of the grace of God.

Jesus as God is a false offense both to Jews and to right-thinking Gentiles. The Trinity as tritheism is similarly a false offense; Incarnation, however—God's way of revealing and fulfilling His purpose to foster the fellowship of forgiveness and the new community in grace—can never be a false offense. If Jesus is presented rightly—as pointing to the God of love from within his own life and teachings—and the Jews are then offended, it can be only because of their own historic background or because God has actually drawn near and they feel

themselves judged and scandalized by His presence. Evangelism to the Jews literally means speaking the truth as it was in
Jesus. But the truth must ever be spoken in love by those who
walk "even as he walked" because they are members of the
same community and know the reality of the power and presence of the Holy Spirit.

We have to be careful, of course, not to preach Jesus after
the flesh. The historic Jesus, at best, is a vague figure. The Jews
look at him through the dank mists of centuries of persecution
in his name by those who have confessed him. Joshua Liebman, author of *Peace of Mind*, accepted God's love as ultimate. He even exulted in *Agape*. Another eminent leader
among the Jews has pressed me to remain urgent and stead-
fast in my proclamation of God as *Agape*. But Liebman failed
and others fail to find in the Jesus figure the fullness of the
love which he is supposed to have taught. "Did he truly and
fully love the Pharisees who opposed him and if so what evidence of this do we have?" they ask. "Was his vision universal?
How much has late reporting twisted his figure and his
words?" We cannot answer these questions fully; and honesty
forbids our making faith judgments about historic facts. Here
we must be tentative. But dominantly there must be a historic
correlation between the Christ and the human person, the
Word and the flesh. Jesus' "weakness of the flesh" was not to
be thought of as comparable to our sins and weaknesses. The
power of his life proves that.

The same is true of the question of Jesus' resurrection.
Surely it seems appropriate that he after whom our age is
named and through whom the *Agape* of God became a historic
power was allowed to return to earthly life in some way in
order to encourage his followers and to help sustain the preach-

ing of the Gospel of the grace of God. History makes such a judgment probable. But we *know* neither that this event actually happened nor exactly what took place. What we do know is that God drew nigh in Jesus, fulfilling our fullest needs to know and to be, with such power that the New Testament was written and the Church was established and prevailed. We *know* no more and must be honest with ourselves and with our facts. Then we can speak the truth in love. If we can win the Jews to this God and to this community in the Holy Spirit, then we shall be able to search together for whatever facts can be validly reported with regard to actual history.

There is no reason, furthermore, why the Jews should not accept this God who works fulfillingly through Incarnation while yet remaining Jews culturally. History shows the need for cultural pluralism. Christianity began among the Jews and can perhaps be released with an unexampled power by the Jewish community when it understands and accepts the Gospel of the grace of God. Then Jewish parochialism will become Jewish particularism, but within a universal perspective and power. The universal Church of the Living God will then have as its proud branch the Jewish Church of Christ, or of the Living God.

There is no solution of the Jewish problem except within the truth. There is no other truth ultimately than the God who is Love. There is no by-passing Incarnation as God's basic relation with the world: creating, sustaining and transforming Love. The Jews, too, have beginnings of such an approach in their own pre-Christian history. In Philo, Jesus ben Sirach, or even in the Old Testament, for instance, the transcendence is broken through and a more intimate relation with the world is prepared by an agent of God in the world who in some sense possesses the qualities of God. As far as His love becomes regnant, all His children will serve Him together in creative joy, but they will also serve Him in the individuating freedom and self-being which He purposed in creation. Christ waits for Judaism. Judaism needs Christ. God waits for both Christians and Jews to live, to know and to proclaim the basic Reality of the Church of the Living God. Ours must be an urgent but humble evangelism of speaking the truth in love.

Speaking the truth in love is also a prerequisite to an evangelism to non-Christian religions. Whereas Judaism has a direct relation to the Christian faith, Hinduism has an indirect relation to it. At its highest, Hinduism is good and wise. The Christian faith cannot be proved impotent because of frightful historic situations which center in the countries where Christianity has reigned. The refutation to such an accusation is that it has not reigned. The sociological backwardness of India, similarly, cannot be used as evidence that Hinduism is mere idolatry. If we are to obtain a religion for one world, a prerequisite is that we understand what is best in each religion, its fullest truth, and not only the actual failures of the persons and people who practice it.

Hinduism at its heart is simple. Reality at its heart is good: saccidananda, i.e., the content of the absolute, is being plus intelligence plus bliss. Brahman, the absolute as such, is beyond all personal individuation and all historic change. Brahman remains ever itself but also periodically produces that which is other than itself. The trick of truth and the health of life are to discover that our empirical selves and our changeful world are unreal. We can do so only by discovering that basically we belong to the absolute, are, in fact, the absolute.

When man knows the truth of "thou art that," he finds salvation, the release from the oppression of the relative. The spell of evil illusion is broken.

Since man's soul is eternal, Hinduism goes on to say, he cannot escape being. He is uncreate in essence. Man's reason is consequently never offended by some irrational creation from nothing, as in Christianity. Man's kind of living, however, depends upon his deeds, his decisions. He is ever half-free and half-determined. The cards of life are dealt to him according to the way he has played the game of life, but what new cards he will get depend upon the way in which he plays each new hand. The universe is just. Some are born again according to their desert as animals, others as inferior human beings, others as superior creatures, others as gods; while those who finally attain, escape being reborn altogether, entering instead into the rest and reality of saccidananda.

The place which one occupies in society is due to one's previous kind of living. One always deserves his actual status. The way to improve it is not to rebel against it in this life, but so to accept one's lot and so to use it that one thereby merits a better one. One may use the way of work, the way of knowledge or the way of committed devotion. But all ways must lead, for release from the rounds of suffering, to the final understanding of the nature of reality and of one's true place within it. Such understanding leads to redemption from the world and the finding of the peace and reality which is one's true nature and possible destiny.

It is easy to criticize this point of view, particularly if one has never thought long and deeply on ultimates in relation to our actual world. Hinduism is, however, a high view of reality and of possible personal nature and destiny, combined with a

vigorous acceptance of the actual. Hinduism can be dismissed
as the rationalization of the caste system. Or oppositely it can
be accused of being an escape from life into a projected illusory
well being. But more careful thinking will likely show this
religion to be generally realistic on the score both of the reality
of the spiritual and of the acceptance of the actual. What a
spiritual people, too, this religion has produced, or, perhaps
what a religion a very spiritual people has produced! They
combine intensity of conviction with tolerance of difference.

No wonder little headway has been made with the evangel-
ization of the leaders of the Hindu people. Our greatest Christian gain, as a whole, at least, has been with the most oppressed
and least thoughtful. On the contrary, Hinduism has spread
rapidly to the West, especially among its intellectuals. What
the relation is between certain Greek philosophies and Hinduism and its progenies, one hesitates to say. A learned scholar
has suggested, producing some possible evidence, that Jesus
may have come under the influence of missionaries from India,
as did perhaps the Essenes. (Compare, for instance, Asoka's
inscription 250 B.C. of Buddhist missionaries sent to Egypt,
Greece and Syria.) Whatever may have happened then, it is
certain that within the last one hundred and fifty years Hindu
ideas have spread rapidly into the West. Buddhism is also
making a real impact on the Occidental mind. As we move
into the possible era of "one world," missionary activity may
less and less become a one-way street.

Have we, then, a real evangel relevant to Hinduism? If so,
this must be based on Incarnation. We can proclaim a personal Spirit as ultimate, and thus tie on to the teachings of
Ramanuja rather than of Sankara—the former Hindu scholar
teaching more of a personal while the latter taught a more

pantheistic ultimate. As a matter of fact, even pantheism can yield its proper proportion of truth when we understand the passivity of God in creation and history as well as the personal presence of the eternal Love in the community and in special providence. A more basic view of God than we now have, in any case, can forcibly grapple with dominant Hindu problems, for the purpose of learning as well as of teaching. Here we need to develop our idea of the Christian God beyond the mere Hebraic view.

The crucial question with reference to evangelism to the Hindus, as to the Jews, will ever be Incarnation *in its conclusive sense. Incarnation shows a personal realm and relationship to be ultimate.* God is definitely determined as being of this very nature—namely, Agape. The personal Word of Agape shows up our sin, as both alienation from and rebellion against God, as both faithlessness and transgression. Sin requires forgiveness; forgiveness, grace. The Christian evangel is the good news of the centrality of the grace of God as it has been displayed in the life, death and resurrection of Jesus. What matters most is not the events in the life of Jesus as past but the possible relation to God which each one may have who through him believes in God.

This personal Spirit, God as Agape, is central to Christianity. Immanence and mysticism, on the other hand, the absolute's being as basically in us as we are in it, and our self-discovery of this identity, are native to Hindu thinking. These Hindu views, however, are feelers for the further and different truth that we can be in God—and are made to be in God—not by *the discovery* of what we truly are now, but, rather, by *the transformation* of what we are now by our becoming radically born anew from above. Such birth is not by illumination and release, although both are involved in the Christian event, but rather by God's personal confrontation of our sinful self, offering us free forgiveness, moral transformation, re-motivation and the experience of the new kind of community in Him for which we were created. We call this confrontation in Christ Incarnation since it centers in God's becoming per-sonal in human history. Perhaps it is particularly to the Hindus that we need to preach Jesus, simply and directly, and we can do so without idolatry provided that we always think of the Word made flesh as inclusive *Agape*, and provided that the direction of our Gospel is through Jesus Christ to God, the eternal Lord and Father of us all.

Hinduism needs this personal note, this sense of sin, this power of forgiveness, this experience of being born again into a new relation with God and men. Within this context, per-sonal *karma* (deed) can be expanded into social *karma*, while *karma* can itself become organically related to *dharma* (social obligation), even while all are basically related to God. Christ becomes the cornerstone of a new community, not as the arbitrary offense based on a false supernaturalism or on a specious transcendence, but as the unexpected fulfiller of Hinduism's best insights and strivings. Neither transcendence nor immanence gives the proper context to truth: only In-carnation. The Christian doctrine can both correct and fulfill the Hindu version of it.

Hinduism has many stresses which we need to make more emphatic: man's basic relation is to ultimate reality; religion is always central to life; reality is morally just, and as a man sows so shall he reap; man's origin is not human birth, but eternity; and his destiny is not death, but eternity. Can these truths of Hinduism be denied in their essential meaning and

depth? Hinduism, however, needs the Christian evangel that
reality is social at its heart; and that love finds satisfaction
through vicarious work. Here Hinduism needs correction and
fulfillment. Man's destiny at its highest, furthermore, is moral
and personal, communion rather than union; this is a note
Hinduism needs. This destiny is possible only because of God's
work in creation, self-disclosure, redemption and fulfillment
through Christ and the Holy Spirit, or through His own presence and power in human life and history.

In our evangelism, however, we must be most careful to
learn as well as to teach. Thus we reflect not only the humility
but also the openness and honesty of love. Traditionalistic
eschatology in Christianity, for instance, is crude and immoral
in comparison with eschatology in Hinduism, lacking its keen
sense of inviolable justice at the heart of the universe. And
who, having pondered eternity long and well, can insist on our
present kind of individuality after death? Have we not even
now known the experience of transcending our usual awareness of individuality when we are lifted into the presence of
God, and that with relation to both our personal and our
communal reality? Anyone who has known the indescribable
experience of ecstasy in communion with God is loath to make
our earthly consciousness the norm for our experience beyond
the grave. Although absorption is no answer to eternity, neither
is the perpetuation of our frail and feeble individuality. Personal immortality, resurrection, life after death, by whatever
name, is transformation as well as mere perpetuation and fulfillment.

In many areas of both theoretical and practical thinking we
can also sit at the feet of Hindu Christianity or, shall we say,
the Hindu branch of the Church of the Living God. Our

evangelism may not be so much a transposition of Christian theology to India as the witness in mature love and reflection to the God who is ever eternal Love and to the kind of community which by grace can be created in Him. Who He is and what this community may become are open areas for the growth of the Gospel within the common grace of God. Our witness to God's Christ in the Holy Spirit may include the witness through humble learning, not because of inner uncertainty and weakness, but because of the nature of our strength and assurance, within the love of God, which to all eternity cannot be exhausted by the creative response of man.

What evangelism to Buddhism involves does not need to be considered at length, save as an attitude. Hinduism is ethnic. Buddhism is a universal religion. Buddhism shares with Hinduism a preoccupation with the salvation of individuals. This statement may seem untrue to those who know Buddhism. Guatama, the founder of Buddhism, insisted that concern with one's own salvation was a supreme form of selfishness. This warning may be heeded by numberless Christians. But actually, the main stress in Buddhism is release from suffering and sorrow on *the part of the individual* through his understanding that the self is not real, and through his attainment—by way of the preparatory eightfold path of right thinking, right believing and so forth—of release into *nirvana* from the unreality of this life. This reality cannot even be thought or understood in terms of our categories of good and evil, for it is always "not this, not this," but is rather that incomprehensibly beyond, that peace of our deepest sleep. We could say that *nirvana* was inescapably better than the fourth state of dreamless sleep, except for the fact that "better" uses our categories of comparison and deep sleep is still an analogy drawn from the kind of experience from which we must be released.

Classic Buddhism generally lacks the outgoing concern of love. Its love is ceasing fom hatred for the sake of finding inner release from desire. Its aim, to be sure, is not individualistic or selfish, but its locus for finding truth and its understanding of ultimate reality both lack the acceptance of the personal-spiritual realm with its capacity for finding satisfaction precisely within the self-giving love of God. It has no positive ultimate who is personal Love and no ultimate salvation within an eternal community of Love. Buddhism, rather, locates our captivating illusion in our sense of selfhood. It knows that life is miserable, because it is selfish. It concludes that therefore we must escape from under the miseries of this kind of self-perpetuating life, here and in lives to come. It does not know the desire of outgoing love to give, to serve and to make others happy. One longs for it to know the positive nature of God as Love, the pedagogical nature of history and of our cosmic setting, the redemptive nature and work of Christ and the kind of community within which the person can lose his preoccupied, miserable self to find his real loving, joyful self.

We are miserable as selfish strivers, even as Buddhism contends. We must lose ourselves. We must work to this end in terms of right understanding and right relation to reality which alone can give real release. How deep and essential Buddhism is! No wonder that it has had such a universal significance in world history as the molder of much of Asia. When the evangel of God in Christ comes, however, to speak to these depth understandings, they are seen not as an external brittle dogma,

frightening away the thoughtful and spiritually sensitive, but
as a psychologically true picture of reality. When the evangel
of God in Christ comes all that is true in Buddhism can become fulfilled. Then we shall have an evangelism in a new
dimension, one that presupposes the development of a whole
new range and depth of theology within the Church of the
Living God. The Buddhist religion will contribute from among
its wise and ancient teachings to the new creative faith, thereby
putting us all in its debt.

I believe that God in Christ as self-giving Love creative of
fellowship constitutes the nature of ultimate reality. Buddhism
may have glimpsed this in its legend that the Buddha sur-
rendered his own chance to enter nirvana in order to teach
suffering humanity the way to escape from its sorrows and the
way to ultimate peace. Such compassion for the world is truly
different from the mere curbing of desire for the sake of finding nirvana.

Buddhism has in fact not been impervious to the truth of
this its central legend. In its later expanded and developed
form Mahayana Buddhism stressed compassion and inclusive-
ness as its two main characteristics. If only the prophetic and
the personal elements had been strong enough to give us one
eternal God, Creator and Judge, whose piercing judgment
focuses the depth and seriousness of sin and whose austere
love makes possible a new dimension of effective community!
God, sin, Christ and the Church have an irrevocable place in
ultimate truth which never became filled even in Mahayana
Buddhism. But without question, both compassion and in-
clusiveness are already there as a basis for communication.
Buddhism can, therefore, now become dimensionally different
in its relation to Christianity, if the inclusive love of God

becomes our own actual operating message and way of behaving. We have so spiced the bread of love which we offer them, however, with myth and prejudice—historic, dogmatic and cultural—that few Buddhists taste much of the proffered loaf.

Let the positive passion for human welfare become central to evangelism, not so as to make reality a means to man's satisfactions, but so as to make man's satisfaction impossible of attainment apart from the full surrender of himself to this redemptive love. If this redemptive passion, rooted in reality, becomes central to our lives, we shall find a new security within which we shall know better the nature of the Christ and the winning power of the Holy Spirit. We shall also find a calm assurance diligently to study and honestly to accept whatever is right and strong and real in other religions. We shall then give this its proper place within God's wider and deeper truth for the world and within the riches of the flexibly full community of the Living God. The grace of God which brings salvation to all men has appeared. Let us be alert and alive to its meaning and power for a new world in Christ.

VI

Light for Communists and Other Pagans

*They also went . . . into all Houses where in sundry fash-
ions men tried to find and to live in the Light. As they
kept telling the good news of the Light their joy increased,
and the time being ready, there was a great and joyful exodus
from all Umbrellas and Houses into the Light.*

To most people evangelism means preaching salvation to
the unconverted, by the unconverted being meant not nominal
Christians or adherents of other religions but the secular
world. Thus the secular world is often equated with the un-
churched. Those who do not generally support Church services or Church projects show themselves thereby to have cen-
tered their interest elsewhere. They are loosely grouped as
secularists. Many outside the Church, however, like Abraham
Lincoln, may believe in God and carefully read the New Testament; they may be people of prayer and personal devotion who
have rejected the institution as not representative of God's
presence and work on earth. Without doubt they recognize
the reality and need for the sacred. But because they do not

attend church or make public confessions of faith, they can be roughly classified as secular.

More truly secular, however, are those who feel no need for religion or who are confused and vague about a religious faith. These secularists may be more concisely described as those who profess no religion. A third kind of secularists are those who consciously, deliberately and persistently reject religion as superstition. They may be sophisticated and condescending or they may be aggressive and argumentative, but they have no hesitation about the outright dismissal of religion as a normal, necessary, desirable part of human life.

Many from all three categories find social substitutes for the religious life; they seek some different kind of response to ultimate Reality. The substitutes for the worship of God may be intellectual-literary. They may be philanthropic-reformist. They may be social clubs with a religious aspect to them. It is hard to live solely for self. It is hard to live apart from some ideal relation or commitment to the environment. It is hard not to satisfy the religious drive. Most people also find some way to glorify themselves in their own eyes in terms of their services to good causes or their memberships in social service groups. Secularists find substitutes for the religious which they invest with sacred meaning and on which they bestow sacred affection. Secularists are often for this reason among our best-living people, upright, pleasant, philanthropic and genuine. We need these people for Christ. Christ needs these to find themselves. God wants them for the world.

We have, in fact, at least three categories of people in Christian lands who need evangelism. Christians need to be evangelized until their lives glow with the truth of the Gospel. None is so near God that he does not need the fuller presentation of the Gospel and the better persuasion to let it mold his entire life. The nominal Christians need desperately the reality of what they so readily and yet reluctantly profess. Such ambivalence frustrates both inner satisfaction and outer usefulness. Reality is blocked off; spiritual energy is short-circuited.

But evangelism is particularly needed for the secularly minded, including the many who are too honest to go along with what they cannot wholeheartedly and wholeheadedly accept. That these people are very good to live with and possess an enviable inner integrity is a fact many church people like to ignore. Such should not be the case if the Church is as necessary as is usually claimed and if conscious religion is necessary to high morality. Yet it is hard to gainsay such a question as this: If religion is basically true and necessary, why do so many leaders in educational and civic life, of outstanding personal rectitude and with a fine outlook on life, fail to recognize either the claim of religion to truth or its necessity for life?

Can it be that these people have sense and honesty enough to see through the sham of ordinary religion, and sufficient inner poise and power to reject it for themselves? The community of the Living God needs especially to court these people, for there is much health and reality in them. But how can we present the evangel to them? The evangelistic message that presupposes the acceptance of Biblical thought forms will fail to reach them, in most instances, because they are too sharply aware of the imperfect parts of the Bible and too honest with the truth. An emotionalistic appeal will turn their deeper selves against the religious invitation. Is there, then, a form of evangelism to the secularized that will truly be effective?

The answer is very simple. The only kind of evangelism that

will convince those who are secular because they can no longer believe in institutionalized religion as it now is, or because they are confused about the truth of the claims of religion, or because they are even sure that the truth is not to be found through religion, is the humble, careful, competent witness to truth. Most people have drifted away from the Christian religion, or have never been reached by it, because the truth has not been given them in forms which they can understand or accept. Myth, dogma and emotion as such are dead end streets for these people. Therefore evangelism must be carried on through every possible channel of communication. The truth must be presented through such channels as schools, social clubs, community discussion groups, church-sponsored forums and through writing, broadcasting and other means of communication. Many, perhaps most, of these secularists will not darken a church door. They must first be reached; and then convinced that the Church is ready to repent and honestly to seek what is real and valid. They must find intellectual freedom, honesty and rigor rather than dogmatic defensiveness within a community before they can wholeheartedly unite with it.

But how can truth be presented to those who live under the secular Umbrella without begging the whole question? How can we show both real interest in them and also real respect for their honesty and intellectual competence? Perhaps we can help them by showing them their own Umbrella. Secular intellectuals, that is, make Truth their god. In doing so, they are also far from entirely wrong. Light has come and does come from those who use reason as the Way to God. Intellectual integrity is a necessity of pure religion, and the right use and reliability of reason are involved in the commandment to worship the Lord our God with all our mind. The humility and beauty of the lives of those who have worshiped the God of truth also bespeak the practicality of this Way. Have not many become martyrs for truth? The Spirit of truth also witnesses to the need for this way of approaching Him.

All the same, the usual result is that God tends to disappear behind the façade of man's intellectual constructions. Faith for those who worship truth and not God becomes more a matter of right thinking and less a matter of trusting God; man's own mind increasingly becomes the standard of truth. If man can prove God's existence, He must be there; if man cannot thus prove His existence, he can no longer believe in Him. Not God, but man, is assumed as most real. In the same manner as man needs to walk in the way of righteousness without putting the Law in the place of God, even so he ought to think both critically and creatively concerning his faith without putting his final trust in Reason. Man's Reason, like man's Law, becomes a House which, however strongly constructed, hides God.

In much the same manner, too, man has made Science his Absolute. Many came to believe that God had to be tested by observed facts. If science found no God, man had to give Him up, whatever his feelings of grief and relief. Many continued to confess God while worshiping at the holy altar of Fact. Their holy of holies was the Scientific Method and its temple was built of well-tested conclusions. It is admittedly true that no genuinely established fact can ever contradict a true and adequate faith. True fact and true faith belong together. If our knowledge of God can be hurt by genuine science, then we ought to give up our faith in God in order to find a faith which is consistent with the most fully established facts. We must live honestly by truth. Obscurantism is no religious virtue.

But science is a limited method dealing with only part of experience. It is neither metaphysics nor theology. If, indeed, God could be proved by science, then science would have to be more real than God and would be, in effect, our God. Confused between science and faith, and also meaning to worship the God of truth while subconsciously fearing to have Him too near, many effectively shut Him out behind systems of science which did not and could not deal with the final question of His being and reign. Most secularists are, of course, not intellectuals, but innumerable people in the modern world have subtly imbibed the general attitude that hardheaded, competent thinking and careful science have discredited religious faith. They must be shown that they also live under Umbrellas. But how can they be convinced of this?

No one can be convinced against his will. Perhaps the first point to be made with those who want to see is that all men are religious. If they genuinely see and admit to themselves this basic truth, evangelism has found the key to their lives even though no door has as yet been opened. Religion is our relation to reality; and all have that! Religion is our own constant choice of what within our experience is most important and most real. Religion is not a matter of some esoteric sect. It is not a matter of some strange experience which is not common to all men. Religion is no extraordinary feeling or behavior. Religion is not a matter of being gullible about some unprovable ultimate, some fancied supernaturalism or some different kind of believing. Religion is not acting according to some sets of belief or practices which are arbitrarily and artificially imposed upon some group.

Religion is, rather, the way in which each one of us and we all together decide to live and to believe. Whether we admit it or not or whether we are conscious of it or not, we all relate ourselves to life through decisions and acts from some position which we cannot fully prove. Every one of us must have presuppositions for thinking and orientation for living. Once I was to deliver a series of lectures at a leading university. Although the president and his wife did not attend any of the lectures, they gave a tea where we met and talked. The president's wife asked me about my lecture on faith and reason. I explained my position point by point. When I was through she said: "But when do you bring out that queer kind of stuff?" By "queer kind of stuff" she meant religious faith. To many people religion is not man's necessary relation to reality and what this involves, but some "queer stuff" which must be dragged in, no matter how much sense may be uttered in preparing for it!

Not only is man inescapably religious, but he also lives necessarily by faith. Freedom is real. Man, to be sure, is not totally free; but he is responsibly free. He is not without conditioning factors within and without; but he is accountable for the choices that he can make. Man is caught in liberty; his freedom is forced on him; he cannot get rid of it; he cannot delegate it; he must live and face the consequences of living. He must decide and face up to the consequences of his decisions. Even evasion into spiritlessness is decision and deep death.

Life is earnest. Life is real. Man must choose and that without seeing clearly the full consequences of his choice. Man acts within ambiguities of emotional pressures which warp and discolor his thinking in all areas of vital personal interest.

Man acts within the tensions which distort his thinking in all spheres of social interest. But not only within is there hesitancy and crossing of lines, but also without, the facts of experience give no clear verdict. No clear light is ever given for all of living and yet man must maintain some kind of stance in order to be a sound individual. Complete drifting is moral disease.

A man may stand firm in one stance, and from there, as far as possible, direct his actions in all areas of concern. Such a stance suffers from frozen decision; it results in a tight, frigid, defensive kind of life. Or he may walk like a caged lion within a given path; his responses and decisions vary in accordance with certain set factors in the outside situation. Or he may stand on a high observation platform from which he may freely view his environment and dexterously choose the best directions in which to move. But wherever he stands, he acts upon presuppositions and axioms of life, many of which are subconscious. What he is least analytical about is what he takes most for granted. But for every morally sound person there are presuppositions for both thinking and living. There must be a stance of some kind; it is never merely given but always chosen in relation to what is given. The stance is most truly the person himself.

Such necessary choice of position is a great truth of existentialism, a point which we must ever keep in mind. Man is not only naturally religious, but he also lives inescapably by faith, and life is a matter of choosing a stance of some kind. Where we stand and what we see depends greatly upon what interests us. Moreover, points of view are never absolute, but are always conditioned by our concrete choices, choices which cumulatively build up our experience in the total of our responses to reality.

This forced freedom, moreover, has to choose ultimates which cannot be empirically observed and controlled. Life is always greater than any finite liver. Reality far exceeds every moral creature. It was there before and will remain after he leaves this life. He will see a snatch of it and will clear a patch of it. He will straighten out a bit of its nature in his own mind. But he who does not understand that the illimitable realities defy his own mastery and outstrip his own understanding of them has committed a deep and dark sin. The grand horizons he has failed to see because of his myopic concentration on a bit of temporal illumination. Does he know that there are horizons which preclude our ever seeing the world all at once? And what of the worlds beyond our world and the realities beyond all worlds?

Such a man is like Kierkegaard's rich man who rides in a carriage so brightly lit as to hide from him the distant stars and mysterious reaches, while the poor peasant trudges the hard road in the dark but within the distant glory of the heavenly places. Rationalism puts reason in a strait jacket and ties the self down with it. For no ultimate can be proved by what is less than ultimate. The ultimate not only authenticates itself in experience but also throws light into all the worlds which, perforce, must be related to it. To prove the ultimate by something more ultimate is to declare the first ultimate spurious or to destroy the meaning of logic. Therefore, every man must live by faith. The real question is not whether or not to live by faith, but rather: "By what kind of faith shall I live?"

Not only is the secularist religious, but he also lives primarily by faith. His forced freedom is accountable, for it sets the stance from which he lives and sees. He must, therefore, for his own sake, be made to see this fact and to acknowledge it to himself. Living is serious business, for himself, for others and for the history of man. The secularist should be helped to see that the deepest concern centers not in our living but in the will of God. What really must be pressed home wisely and competently is that religion is not optional, that we all must live primarily by faith, that our choices matter not only to us but also to others.

Then we must go on to show that faith can be authoritative without being arbitrary, that true faith fulfills reason, that only an adequate absolute can genuinely explain the becoming, the meaning and the end of our cosmic process and the purpose of history as a whole and of every human life. Only those who are competently grounded in the truth can communicate it and show the necessity of an ultimate not only of stance but of Reality. Surely when truth captures faith it will satisfy the mind. We must start with mind, not because it is central, but because many secularists cannot let themselves believe until they are deeply satisfied that what they believe is the truth.

It is impossible, however, to prove that the Christian faith is ultimate truth, both because reason is a variable modifying the self as another variable, and because the world as we find it gives only mixed indications concerning the nature of what is most real. But to the spirit seeking truth, in simplicity and without defensiveness, the Christian faith can be shown to be more plausible than any other candidate for ultimate truth, to be the most reasonable context for thought. To those of a contrite and humble heart the greatest insight into the reason for creation, for history, for suffering, for evil and the nature and problems of personality and society can be found within the love of God.

Those who have learned the ultimacy of community and of personality find in the content of God's love the kind of community and personal experience which are most congenial to the human spirit and most organic to the human setting. Those who need to face the fullness of human suffering and sin find in the meaning of the Cross the most seminal clue to process both as pedagogical and redemptive. Those who have faced the new universe of science can find a God within the Christian faith far greater than the ever-creative stellar spaces of modern astronomy.

Proof would preclude faith. Perfect sight would prevent decision. The nature of the Christian faith makes clear why intellectual demonstration beyond ambiguity in spiritual matters would block growth and make freedom unreal. And yet the Christian faith alone makes possible the fullest seeing and the freest living. We shall always have rationalists, on the one hand, and skeptics, on the other, who when proof is impossible will surrender reason rather than make full use of it within the living decisions of committed and open faith. But wisdom is justified only by those who live it!

Besides giving intellectual sense to the world we confront, the Christian faith can give power in practical life. As a matter of fact, intellectual light waits upon living truth. The more that problems are solved within one's personal life in terms of the deep satisfaction of God's purpose for us, the more intellectual light becomes available as well. The more that social problems are in process of solution the more truth is given as a kingdom in which to reign and to serve. The more that personal and social sins and defects are forgiven and corrected the more community is achieved and personalities evolved who testify to truth more by who they are than by what they say. This testimony of truth is the only effective evangelism to the secular mind.

Yes, truth is more a matter of being than of seeing, more a matter of walking than of talking. Truth is teasing to be known and yet we leave her alone, because our witness is to ideals and not to Incarnation. The secular mind does seek salvation. Its fleeing from God is only part of its movement. At the same time it makes exploratory adventures to find reality. When it meets those who claim to have found meaning, peace, power, purpose, satisfaction and genuineness it looks and listens. It usually hears high-sounding claims but sees low-flying lives. It usually compares claim to life with the life itself. The theoretical fails to convince. Lives that have found and lived the truth move the world.

A few powerless wanderers on the face of the earth and history rise to emulate such men as Jesus and St. Francis. Schweitzer seeks his soul in service which pinnacles his thinking as well as his living. The world needs salt and not sauce, the tang of Christian reality and not the sweets of its promises. It needs more service than services, for true service comes out of the whole heart whereas services often substitute for the serving which we ought to do. The winning witness is working worship. Let the Church be the Church in its inner life and in its living with the world and the world will be made new through worship. How better can the living truth as it was in Jesus ever be proclaimed? Is this not the effective way to preach Christ to the world?

A wise teacher knows that we learn most easily what is pleasant. The whole world longs for genuine peace and joy. The original Christian community grew apace because its members were possessed by an irrepressible joy. This joy was not dependent upon physical well-being or social acceptance. The early Christians overflowed with joy in the midst of their sufferings and persecutions. They sang exultantly in prison at midnight—and in what prisons! They had peace in the face of the loss of everything, even in the face of death. They lived in the power of the Light and the light in their faces could not be denied. Today, too, nothing will convict and convince unbelievers so much as the joy and peace of believers. Authentic Christian lives have power to win beyond measure. We usually lack such power. We call others to the death of self without being able to show them a life abundant and glorious beyond that death. Usually we fail to win converts because our own Umbrellas of self are still widely spread. Nothing carries the power for Christ more convincingly than authentically radiant Christians.

Even a kindled life, however, cannot win the world until it be grounded in the most solid fastnessnes of intellectual truth. Knowledge is vision and without vision the people perish. Life lived apart from its own understanding witness to truth has real power to move, but not the fullest strength to lead. Truth must be taught as well as caught, seen as well as felt, in the largest and clearest possible tapestry of real relations. Thus no amount of living can take the place of study. Many who stress "life" do so to avoid meeting a real need for competent thinking. When both of these facets—truth for the mind and truth for life—are done with their work, however, the most important factor and the most neglected function for effective evangelism to the secular world has still been left out: the Holy Spirit.

It is now fashionable to discuss communication. Some insist on the indirect method of "wounding from behind," the indirect presentation of the truth. Some speak of story as the best form; others advocate the use of symbols. All of these have their place, to be sure, but there is no winning to the truth ever to be compared to the wooing of the Spirit of Truth. The Spirit speaks through the mind, for He translates and transmits our Gospel to the secular mind to convict of sin and to reveal poverty of soul before the message can be rationalized away. The Spirit also speaks through Christian living, thereby transpowering the message.

The Spirit speaks most deeply through the feelings. To be sure, we decide in the light of reason, but we *live most deeply through the confirmation of our feelings*. The feelings carry the tones of satisfaction and dissatisfaction into that total complex of responses which is the ever-present context of living. The mind sees a truth, accepts it and reports back to the total self. The self feels itself and its relation to reality. When the report comes in, the self compares the import and impact of this thought with its total relation to reality. If the thought agrees generally with what the self already believes and can enhance the self, it may be accepted and used for what it is worth to the total self. If the thought is disagreeable, the self may not dismiss it offhand, but warily feel around it, weighing it in relation to its total feeling-stance, in order to ascertain whether whatever correction it suggests may improve the satisfactions of the self.

If the cost is not too heavy, the self may accept the irritation which its inclusion may make in the reservoir of feeling, or in the dynamic master complex of life. In such a manner the self grows and adjusts itself to its world, not always pleasantly but sometimes also with pain. Often thoughts are reported which reveal external situations which the self can neither master nor change, thoughts which make seemingly impossible demands on the self. Then the self may shut out such reports by repressing them below the threshold of conscious awareness and choice. It banishes the report, as far as it can, to permanent exile. Thereupon a guard is placed at the entrance of this region of the self. Thus the acting self shields itself, if it can, from what is unbearably unpleasant. It may break in the attempt. Or it may apparently keep going normally, so far as society goes, but with spiritlessness and lack of conviction. Sometimes it will undergo deep inner tension which is focused by the depth conscious on secondary causes to keep the real cause hidden.

Religion is our relation to reality. It is always our prime stake in life. Therefore, we feel most deeply about our religion. But we may so wall off our frustrations or depth evasions that both to others and to ourselves we appear to have little interest in it. We are dogmatic, aggressive and defensive, and inflict pain on others because of the substitutes which we have made serve as our gods. We lack drive or we become feverishly active. We become neurotically fearful and withdrawn or we go on veritable binges of social intercourse. Our deepest self, however, can never be fooled. These selves either dry up or die of cancerous overgrowths. Sin is the main cause of our misery. Sin is the chief reason for all our Umbrellas. Sin is the rock-ribbed ground for secularism.

Man is unhappy because he is not right with God, because he is partly alienated from reality. Man mourns because he is not real. Man weeps within, tears for a stifled and wasted life, from which the sense of meaning has faded. He lacks joy, peace, satisfaction. Even suffering would be hallowed, if only he knew its real purpose. Even deprivation would water the inner growth, if only he understood its meaning. But he cannot understand, for he will not. Although man's deepest self can never be fooled, he has hidden from himself the cause of his misery. He will not face his sinful faithlessness and rebellion against God and His way. He has shoved the root reason for his suffering down into the dungeon of his life and thrown away the key. He means to be rid of the cause of his feelings of guilt and fear. He means to fashion a world on his own terms and to his own liking. But he fails and suffers. He fails and tries to force happiness. He fails and tries to compel light to rise in his darkness.

The real truth is kept from him within and without by guards which watch the inner castle. Meanings are let in only when they have been made to recant their original import and sworn to make no mention of the hidden regions. Thus words of life are spoken but never heard. The evangel is proclaimed but never understood. The message is preached but the spirit is never reached. The confirmation of feelings which are the central core of the accumulated responses of the self to the world thus go on within the directions of their own choosing, confirming the false path as right and excluding the right path as false.

The idea may come knocking that something Christian ought to be done about race, something costly and crucifying to self. The message is not treated as a serious option; it comes rather as a basic threat to the self; and however much the meaning of the words may penetrate the rational mind, the problem for the self is not at bottom rational, but emotional. Therefore, a mere rational exposition of the faith gets nowhere. Apart from God's grace, directly or indirectly, sin is stronger than reason. He is blind who will not see the truth. Again, the God of all grace and glory is proclaimed unto the remission of sins and the newness of life. This good news has been forced down long ago into the dungeon of self and its full force shut out by the guardians at the door of master motivation. The message is heard with the ears but the hearts are impassive.

What then? What hope is there? How can we possibly evangelize the secular world? There is scant hope in mere rational ideas, however right and real. There is little hope even in the power of example, if it be that alone. There is genuine hope only in the Holy Spirit. For the Holy Spirit has access to the prison, however deep the dungeon of the self. The Holy Spirit passes through all barriers of guards or locked doors. The Holy Spirit always has an ally within the self, but an ally which cannot free the self except as aided by the Holy Spirit.

This ally is the Spirit resident within, the slave who owns the self, but deigns for the self's sake to work as a maltreated servant. By title deed this slave belongs in the house of the self forever. He can never be removed. He is the representative of reality that no person can ever banish. He speaks and pleads in the dungeon where he is not heard by the self, who shuts himself off by means of the heavy walls which lead to the dungeon. He speaks in the feelings, but the self has hardened itself to his constant warnings. He keeps the self from being happy and contented. But he is not allowed to guide it into the reality that can free it, let it find peace and become creatively satisfied.

When the Holy Spirit speaks to this slave from without, the

slave within claims his right to the title deed; then he knows that his time for deliverance from voluntary servitude can cease. It can only cease insofar as the self sees its own mistake in banishing the voice of reality; when it understands and accepts the folly of seeking for self-satisfaction and self-security; when it acknowledges to itself that its destructive tensions are due to its sin of imprisoning its own sense of right and reality; when it comes to admit that God is right, and opens its whole life to the Lord and Master who is really its Father and Friend. In order for this to happen, the self needs to hear the message of deliverance spoken not merely in rational words, which it can keep out, not merely in terms of good life and example, which it can caricature, but spoken in the Holy Spirit, at the very bottom of its existence. Then it can no longer refuse to listen seriously. It still can reject, with suffering and sorrow, the voice of God to its life. It is still free to defy the Father. But it cannot hide from Him. It is forced to decide for or against its God.

The Holy Spirit has made those of us who hear Him into a free community and He will not, for our sake, speak except at our own request. As we believe, love, pray and witness in the Holy Spirit for the full salvation of our fellow men in that they find God real and make their lives right with Him in the truth, we shall see a new day of spiritual revival beyond anything we could ever have dreamed possible. Our real problem is so to live ourselves and to get people to live, pray and love in the Holy Spirit that the prison doors of secularism, behind which the secularists have locked away their true selves, may open wide. Then we shall find a secular world ready for basic conversion and witness a reality of seeing and of living, of loving and of winning, issue forth. The hearts of the faithful will be cheered and strengthened and the lives of nominal Christians will be convicted and converted. Our weary world will wake up in sharp surprise at the power of the Gospel, coming not in terms of man's words and wisdom alone but in the strength and power of the Spirit. So be it! So be it soon!

Evangelism to the secular world can generally count on a backlog of Christian presuppositions. They may be whittled down and devoid of both content and vitality, but there is at least a general acceptance of ethical standards. There is still a community of common ideas, even if the community of ideals has been punctured and the community of common response to reality has been basically ruptured.

But what of the evangelism to Communism? What of evangelism to the eruptive, aggressive antichristian force which discards Christian ideas and ideals as subversive of the welfare of the workers? What of evangelism to those who treat religion as an opiate? What of evangelism to those who though they have discarded metaphysical thinking for relative rules and merely existential commitments, yet do believe in a science of history according to which the eventual victory of their cause is certain?

What of evangelism to a new kind of people within whom long-hallowed and established words like "democracy" and "freedom" have taken on radically altered meaning, not only in thought but in feeling? What of evangelism to a people who not only forbid the Gospel in its full implications but who ruthlessly and cunningly work to eradicate power of any kind except that of the Party? Can there be, realistically speaking, any evangelism to a people who execute those who are caught listening to short-wave radios? What chance do we have when children are taught presuppositions so contrary to Christianity that the Gospel seems sheer superstition and basically irrelevant?

First of all, in order to evangelize Communists we must understand them against their history, ideology and present world situation. The *history* combines the story of widespread martyrdom and amazing success in spite of it. When few Christians sat in prison for their allegiance to the common people, the Communists sat there in large numbers. But from the prisons came forth leaders dedicated to their Cause. And the Cause prospered faster and more mightily than any movement in history. If history vindicates suffering and truth, is it any wonder that multitudes see Communism vindicated by actual events and confirming the predictions of its own ideology?

This *ideology* is basically simple. Truth is scientific, not speculative. Science describes the class structure and the economic processes of history. History moves dialectically according to the possession of the means of production. Original man lived under communism of a very simple kind. When the invention of means of production came about, these means were seized by the powerful, who made the masses work for them, but withheld the rightful earnings of the workers as private profit for themselves. "The capitalists" exploited the workers. Such exploitation deprived the workers of the power to buy or use what they had produced; and therefore overproduction resulted, causing further misery.

Thinking, they say, always rationalizes the historic situation. When the means of production are in the power of the few who exploit the masses, no thinking is generally possible or permitted which does not support the present class structure.

But the inherent weaknesses in this system of exploitation will lead to a widening cleft between workers and owners. The workers cannot, with some possible historic exceptions, better their lot through government by means of appeal, persuasion or organized pressure, because the power is always finally in the hands of the oppressors. Therefore, the only way to a new and better world where oppressive government will not be needed and where the production will be for the common plenty is through ruthless revolt and the smashing of the power of the oppressors. This the Communists believe.

Then, they claim, when man's whole motivational structure is not automatically geared and educated into selfishness, man can be reconditioned to social incentives and common co-operation. *Then* the chains will be cast away, once for all, and men will stand glorious and free, served and not mastered by the machine, coworkers together in the full freedom from selfishness, want and government oppression. In the meantime, there must be ruthless concentration on the overthrow of oppressive governments and the world-wide revolution of the workers. What now seems to be indescribable and heartless oppression is really the relentless outworking of the final right and good of the people against the centers of power, greed and exploitation.

Today, *in the light of the present world situation*, this hope seems fulfilling itself or this faith justifying itself, for they see Communism spreading with unrivaled rapidity and power across the face of the globe and down the length of the century. In peace it penetrates, in war it expands; either way, it becomes the focus of the world's attention. Yet it is threatened by capitalistic military might and technological mastery. Although the Cause cannot be lost, it must yet be won through sacrifice. Therefore, the comrades work and fight on until victory is won and the world is freed. This, I believe, is something of the inside convictions which make the Communist threat a blaze like a forest fire.

What is our own counteroffensive? If we really believe in God, if we truly are captured by Christ, if we are fully convinced that God's eternal purpose for freedom and faithfulness in fellowship is the final power of history—what do we say or do? The Church of the Incarnate Word must answer. Here is one answer.

We must try to reach into Communist lands, as far as we can. If we cannot, the fight must be won wherever Communism has not yet suppressed freedom of speech. We must worship, work and witness to make the Gospel effective in every way, the salt of the earth, both to prevent the spread of Communism and, eventually in God's way, to win back Communist countries. Some pray, think and wonder, day by day, how God is going to let us become more effective in this area. In the meantime, with us and for them, we offer the following leads toward evangelism to Communists who can be reached.

Most of us fail to be effective evangelists because we feel inwardly guilty and for that reason unprepared and ill-disposed to witness to a Gospel which is not real in our own lives. Our own commitment to God in Christ must be unequivocal. We must surrender our lives to His bidding: spirit, mind and body. Position, reputation, personal success, family and life itself must have no power over us to deter us from a full and confident witness both in word and in deed. We must learn to die daily. We must not mind earthly things, for our commonwealth is in heaven.

We must not count our lives as dear unto ourselves in order

that we may fulfill our calling to preach the Gospel of the grace of God. Our treasure and our hearts must be in heaven— in heaven for the world. A member of the Church of the Incarnate Word must not only worship but carry the Cross. Daily he must accept it, making his life a calling beyond any mere work or profession. He must live to introduce men to God. His family must live to introduce men to God. His Church must live to introduce men to God. The new community of the Living God must be real, at whatever cost to self and to the sacred society.

This commitment must include God's burden for the world. Each member must pray from God's point of view for the whole world, collectively and concretely. He must learn to imagine the whole world as living for each one and each one as living for the whole world. He must picture a concrete community where this union is being approximated by the grace of God. He must pray for spiritual power, for intellectual wisdom, for strength in the realm of the socio-political areas of life. No human problem can in essence be foreign to his concern. The more he thus carries the world's burdens and his own, the more he must pray for fuller commitment, even when the going is dreariest and death away from it all seems easier. He must be coworker with Christ and fellow laborer with God with his whole life: imagination, affection and action.

Particularly he must feel at one with the Communists on the level of God's plan and purpose for the world, on the dimension of our common humanity, within the acknowledgment of our shared sinfulness, within the reality of a "one-world" situation, and, above all, within the constraint of love born and nourished in authentic prayer. Without accepting what is false, what comes short and what is evil, he will understand the reason for the rise of Communism, the truth of much of its economic criticism (which is a critique of our sinful human nature as well as the statement of failure in economics) its history and the way Communists now look at the world situation. A member of the Church of the Living Word will have to be both fair-minded and ample-hearted.

He should, of course, unsentimentally see through and reject the half-truths of Communism. History is economically conditioned according to God's purpose in history for us, *but not economically determined.* Class wars are real and the possession of power by one group causes oppression, *but no solution can finally come through conflict, only through co-operation as the ideal and practical force.* Man is corrupted by his property relations and selfishness is encouraged by our system, *but human nature cannot be freed from self-centeredness by the removal of external temptations.* Ambiguities cannot thus be removed from history. To try to do so is either not to understand reality or to defy God's kind of creation. Final victory for man is in the nature of things and the end of history is certain, but the victory is God's final winning, through our understanding and whole-lived acceptance of His purpose for us. Communism is secularized Jewish Messianism. Jewish Messianism is itself God's plan foreshortened to our earthly history. When the secularized version and the earthly location are removed and God's larger plan remains, we shall see truly what underlies man's hope for victory. The community of the Living Word has the perspective in which Communism is both corrected and fulfilled.

Within this larger perspective and commitment, we must thus transcend in prayer the high cliffs that divide us and hold the Communists fast in our love. Prayer for them is as natural as Christian life. Our commitment in Christ is unto death for all men everywhere. Our love is unconditional. We do not depend upon its being answered or how it is answered. We depend upon the God who loves us and calls us. We must, therefore, believe God's promise that prayer is effective, in accordance with our faith, on the other side of any iron or gray curtain. We must raise up a praying people who break down all man-made barriers by the power of the Holy Spirit—in His way and at His pace.

If this cannot be done, our faith is false. If the walls of Russia and China do not fall when the aroused community of the Living God marches around it seven years and seven days—whatever be God's full measure—then we worship local gods and not the God of the whole world and of the universes. We are then like the Jews who, not wanting to fight on the Sabbath and believing in God's protection of an obedient people, let the Romans slaughter them. Our faith in prayer is tested by how we pray for Communist countries to bring their glory not only into the new heaven but also into the new earth.

We must, furthermore, work to show the kind of political front that represents the Christian cause. We must dare to help on the other side, if opportunity occurs, even when the help is misrepresented. We can help the misrepresenters. Some of Christ's real heroes are today the butt of ridicule and the object of the most serious suspicions. We must dare to act on the principle of the faithfulness of God. We must, that is to say, believe in righteousness as the final law of history. Lincoln may be killed by chauvinists but his actions are the salt of history. When the more gentlemanly generals in the Civil War were replaced by the ruthless destroyers "from Atlanta to the Sea," and when vengeful "realists" took control, the evil effects of the war were multiplied. Bismarck yielded to the "realistic" generals and let Metz be taken by Germany in 1870. But the vision of the statesman was truer than the realism of the soldiers, for shortsighted selfishness aggravated the craving for vengeance in France.

We greatly err when we leave God out of account in our practical judgments of politics. We rationalize politics to be only ruthless power based on selfish advantage, but history makes fools of its blind interpreters. If our dealing with the Communists were on the level of right, and not on the level of advantage, material gain and protection, military power and expediency, then history would lead us elsewhere than to deepened anxiety and to the loss of both inner honor and outer poise. When we crossed the Thirty-eighth Parallel in Korea, we galvanized China against us and lost our own sense of right.

The prophets go unheeded and history hurtles from one disaster to the other. But those who know the power of God know that wisdom is justified of her children. Those who truly belong to the Church of the Universal God will have their eyes opened to the truths of history by her vision of the reality of God as its true Ruler. Faith in God for all men is the heart of history's wisdom. If totalitarian oppression can permanently crush Christian faith, then God is not real and Christianity is a first-class lie. If nothing can conquer God's Christ, let us give Him His fullest way through us. Long enough have we trusted in princes and chariots. Let the people now trust God with a revolutionary zeal never before witnessed in human history. Let us outmatch the Communist revolution with the revolution of the Christian community. What better way to preach the Gospel of Christ for a confused world?

For no evangelism can be genuine that does not require our own repentance and demand fruits worthy of repentance from our social and political decisions. The reason that we so fear this materialistic power of Communism is that we are mainly materialistic in our own desires and securities. This power speaks our language, but openly and without hypocrisy. We profess faith in idealism, generosity, righteousness and peace, but our real fears are the fears for our own possessions and power. Certainly we have still the heritage of freedom, and, thank God, much freedom is still real, but when we are threatened, our freedoms tend to disappear. In World War II no constitutional rights could save the freedom of Japanese Americans, many of whom had long been citizens of the land of the free. If we were ourselves in the threatened position of Germany much of our freedom might suddenly and unceremoniously disappear. Certainly we believe in righteousness in general, but what is the criterion of our actions in dealing with the Communists?

The fact is clear. We have spoiled the power of our ideals by our hypocrisy in the very use of terms. We have taken over much of both Communist and Nazi techniques in the manipulation of public opinion. We stand in need of a basic conversion, of a genuine repentance. We need to turn to moral and spiritual sources for inner power and for clarity in dealing with the forces which threaten us.

Besides all this, much war fever or fear of war is based on hysterical fear which flows from lack of inner convictions and of true faith in God. Some of it is also pumped up for political reasons—only the war industry may now keep us from an economic depression! We are deeply ill and act it. No evangelism to the Communists, therefore, can be sincere and effective that does not first recognize our own sins, cause us to repent of them ourselves, accept the community of the Living God, and *in the light of a sweeping moral revolution*, receive the wisdom from above to deal with the forces that threaten us. Surely we shall overcome them by the sword of the Spirit of truth.

For truth will win the final day. Truth will have its own say. Marx sat the long part of his life *writing*. The first edition of *Das Kapital* sold poorly, but he knew in spite of the criticism of his friends that he was making a strong case for revolution. It took long in coming, but it came. At the time of Galileo and Kepler no institution had as much control over men's minds as the Church; despite the opposition of the Church these men knew that truth was with them and they dared the future to deny it. Jesus was crucified and his disciples driven underground, but the truth could not be kept from the world. We must now seek and find the truth for our day, caring not for opposition. We must work out a new theology with creative and critical care. We must be more realistic in our understanding of history. We must have faith in the open and dedicated minds of our competent spokesmen, while raising up more and more competent leaders to confirm or to correct the truth as expressed by the pioneers of the Church of the Living God. For we are living in a period of theological revolution of the deepest historic importance.

But above our commitment and our prayer, above our including the Communists in understanding and our treating them righteously and with winning patience, even above our faith in truth—above all these, we must have faith in God. They have faith in the nature of history. They cannot lose, they believe, because the nature of reality is with them. But we know that God is going to be finally victorious over all men, winning them to His love. We must, therefore, have the faith of our convictions rooted and grounded in the love of God. The Holy Spirit will show us how to speak; He will guide us through opening doors; He will open hearts and minds to truth. There are no barriers which God's love cannot penetrate, if we trust Him. There are no walls that will not tumble when the trumpets of God's believing hosts keep sounding around them day and night. This is our strength, the faith which is our victory, and will overcome even the Communist world. Christ in us is the hope of glory for the world and for the world to come. When He possesses our lives, we shall learn when and how to talk, when and how to write, when and how to keep silent, how to live, how to die and how to rise victorious over anything that men can put in the way of the Gospel.

By their fruits ye shall know them. No prayer, or faith or talk that does not work will ever win the world. To win the world we must prove the genuine love which breaks down social barriers, which refuses to have poverty amidst plenty, which gives free opportunity for all individuals and groups for full, responsible expression and development, which cares concretely and creatively for man as man.

Spiritual commitment we must have, social transformation we must have. Intellectual revolution is required for the new world and the new age. Political cleansing and remaking is a sine qua non. To be sure, we cannot preach ourselves and win the world. We cannot convince the Communists by merely advocating a new start. But as we are obedient to God's righteousness, personal and social transformations will follow. As we worship rightly we shall work advantageously. As we pray genuinely we shall study honestly and creatively. As we surrender all to Christ we shall claim all of life for Him. We shall witness to the Communists because whatever truth is theirs we accept wholeheartedly, and beyond their truth lies God's truth for the world which must judge and save us all.

Evangelism to Communism must presuppose our willingness to make democracy real and rich, here and now. God's love consists not in talk but in power. This power will first make real the Community of the Living God where barriers are erased and effective social relations are created. But even as this community is being made real, it must work as *leaven even more than salt* until all social relations and political decisions are more and more effectively shaped by the power of the revolutionary community in Christ.

Evangelism is God's good news for the world. To believe in the possibility and practicability of a new world order is to show no lack of realism. A world which mainly trusts itself will not and cannot know the power of God. But He is there ready to help if only men will have Him, for the better day in life and for civilization will come *to the extent of our right and obedient faith in God.* We await in faith the new heaven and the new earth, here or beyond this life, where dwells righteousness. We may all fail; the promises of God cannot.

Set in Linotype Electra
Format by Katharine Sitterly
Manufactured by The Haddon Craftsmen, Inc.
Published by HARPER & BROTHERS, *New York*

DR GRUBER'S
DAUGHTER

DR GRUBER'S DAUGHTER

Janice Elliott

Hodder & Stoughton
LONDON SYDNEY AUCKLAND TORONTO

British Library Cataloguing in Publication Data
Elliott, Janice
 Dr Gruber's daughter.
 I. Title
 823'.914[F]   PR6055.L48

 ISBN 0 340 39762 4

Hodder and Stoughton Editorial Office: 47 Bedford Square, London WC1B 3DP.

For Cherry Hastings Bernays

Chapter One

*I*n the Fifties, in England, on a war-torn planet so weary it was a wonder, thought the woman who called herself Ilse Lamprey, it could still turn at all, in the northern reaches of the university city, sallow Ilse Lamprey sat in her wheelchair at her window and tapped the sill with a long varnished fingernail, chipped. Where was Babakov with the Bovril?

From her first-floor window Ilse could see: the spring (which she disliked), a glimpse of the main road through the as yet unburdened chestnuts, the enclave of solid houses and quiet gardens, and the Convent of the Little Flowers of St Anne. A spiritual island, you might say, behind its high walls the object, depending upon her mood, of Ilse's scorn, curiosity and envy. At any sign of action – of which there was little – she would, as now, take off her spectacles and raise her opera-glasses. There was the bell-tower above the chapel, there the dovecote and now quite suddenly the orchard flooded with the bobbing of starched coifs (this was before the freedom) and the air filled with doves – on the ground and under the sky, the whiteness of snow or blossom or handkerchiefs torn from a line. The novices, she assumed. *Dancing?*

Ilse put down the glasses, sighed and, since she was bored with her library book, contemplated the territory within reach of her gaze and frequently her malice. Once there must have been fields here, until the dons, released from their celibacy, built their houses, staked out their blessed plots, planted their rhododendrons and, with the stern enthusiasm of a thousand years of sexual deprivation,

7

set out to people the Empire. Ilse Lamprey imagined their Sunday tables, the great red joints, the apple pies, the prayers of thanksgiving, the sly and pious conceptions in the dark between linen sheets on feather beds which once a year would be taken out and beaten on the line. And the annual childbearing – Ilse shuddered to think of it. I shudder to think of it, she would say to Babakov, her basement lodger, and Babakov would mumble and nod and slip a chocolate digestive into his pocket.

Then times changed. The university rode out the wars as complacently as it had survived the centuries. So many colleges did it contain, so many memorials, books and brains, you could say it was England's memory. So old, so grand it was, it would hardly have noticed when the houses on this northern boundary were sold and divided into two, and sub-divided, like Ilse's, into maisonettes and flats and rooms.

Nowadays, in season, between the heavy chestnuts, silver wheels flashed, girls from the student hostels rode in their summer skirts to tutorials, lectures, assignations; sometimes stood entwined with their young men in the dusk spiked with suburban scents: philadelphus, nicotiana, lilac.

Lilac. There was something most complacent and offensive of all about lilac, its buds now thickening, its provincial cloying sweetness that made Ilse sneeze and remember childhood with pain and fear the future. One night of insomnia and full moon she had been seized at this very window by one of those visions that came to her often now uninvited and unwelcome: she had seen in the strong topmost branches of the Convent lilac, lovers resting like birds in a nest, the boy dark, the girl's breasts shining with moon.

Ilse wheeled herself to the door, hooked it open and shouted: 'Babakov! Bovril!'

Ilse did not like lovers, real or visionary. Ilse was writing a book or preparing to write a book (it was from the time she

announced this fact to herself and to Babakov that the
visions had begun) which would be an astonishing novel
and contain all the things Ilse did not like. In the night she
would wake, put on her spectacles and add to the list she
kept always at hand. So far the list read:

> poached fish
> beautiful girls
> Elenora Flitch
> spring NB lilacs
> modern novels
> Elenora Flitch's cats
> Sunday
> nuns?
> England
> Thursday
> bread and butter pudding

Elenora Flitch's lovers she thought of adding, but had yet
to determine if the figures she had seen circling the house at
night were creatures of her insomnia, Elenora Flitch's
lovers or burglars. Lodgers she had written down but
pencilled through with a query since she was uncomfortably aware that her existence at 161 Radpole Road depended upon those who occupied its rooms. How Ilse,
arriving lame and penniless in England, had come by the
house in the first place was her own business known only
to Babakov and one other, but without the lodgers she
chose not to think what would become of the intricately
woven fabric of her life – it would unravel.

And without Babakov – now clumping his way upstairs,
purblind, hand shaking, slopping Bovril – where would
Ilse be? Dependence of any kind appalled her but who else
would fiddle the rations, hold the house together, collect
the rents, pick up Ilse with such astonishing ease considering his infirmities and carry her on her rare but vital forays
from this room? Who else could extract liver from the

butcher, chop and serve it raw to her taste? Self-pity was allowed neither at Ilse Lamprey's table nor in her bed, nor even entertained to tea. But at the thought of life without Babakov, she saw its wet, silly face.

Here he was now: such a mess. The collarless shirt, the belly slopping out at the waist (one button undone to accommodate it) of the black trousers left over from an evening suit. The trousers, baggy at the knees and shiny with misuse, had a bloom of verdigris. The cardigan gone at the elbows, the watery eyes behind spectacles stuck together with Elastoplast, the puffy white hands clattering the cup upon the saucer as he set down the Bovril. Well, he'd got that right at least. Ilse scorned milk, took her animal fluids strong and dark as if to make up for the secret, meatless years of which she never spoke.

'What you would do without me, Babakov, I can't think.'

'I expect you are right, Ilse Lamprey.' Submission was his role in this house, Babakov knew, though there were times, as now, gazing out of the window at the spring (he could see things distant quite well) when a young man sprang from his body, leaped upon a racing bicycle – keen as the first horse he had ever ridden – pedalled so fast he took off from Radpole Road, from the city, from England, from this poor drab little mid-century, and came to earth in another time and place, flushed and proud, walking with his arm round a girl between hedgerows high and sweet.

'I am sorry. What did you say?' Could she read his mind, he sometimes wondered? Would she reach out with those long talons and rake out his brains? Her eyes were like blackbirds pecking, her teeth sharp. But she had been in her own time a beauty, in an odd way. He might have danced with her. Perhaps he had? To the old man parts of the past were clear and sharp, the rest retrieved only with the greatest difficulty and even then fancy and fact blurred, dream could take on historical certainty one day, the next shimmer and dissolve. Ilse Lamprey might be surprised though, what company he kept in his dark basement room.

Wild times, kind times. He would wake to find his grandmother baking bread. At winter dusk he would look up and see his mother – so small, slim, and upright as a bird on a branch, perched reading on the straight-backed corner chair. She should wear her spectacles. The light had gone. And then the girls who visited his bed! The small breasts, the full thighs, the bites, the laughter, the tricks, the taste, the darting tongues and clever fingers. If Ilse knew.

'Old fool. Dreaming again.' Ilse grunted. She tapped her library book. 'You can take that back, for a start. I have written the librarian a letter I count upon you to deliver. Now. Your report.'

Babakov stood, puffy hands crossed somewhere around his belly-button, if he still had one. He brought from his basement a distinct whiff of kippers.

'I believe the Countess is having Dr Gruber tonight. A little *soirée à deux*. At least, she has obtained a chop, which would indicate Dr Gruber. Janusz Grzyb's month of grace expires today. Will you wish me to extend it, Ilse Lamprey?'

'Give the boy a day or two. What is he up to?'

'That I cannot say. His door is locked. He does not come out.'

Ilse nodded. 'I advised him to master English. Well, go on.'

'Miss Flitch is about to commence a tutorial. A young person is at this moment coming up the drive.'

'Person?'

'Female.'

'My greatest mistake, that woman. We still have nothing on her?'

'Nothing at all, Ilse Lamprey.'

'You have been watchful?'

'Of course.'

'Those cats?'

'Are clean.'

11

'Rent?'

'In advance.'

'Lovers? A woman that age must have lovers.'

'Not in England.'

'You have a point there, Babakov. What a terrible country! Whatever are we doing here? They run neither hot nor cold.'

Babakov pulled his lower lip. He had forgotten to shave this morning. Would she notice? There was, he supposed, something infernal about Ilse Lamprey but since he could imagine no other life he appeared to be tied to her. There was no escaping that. She had bought him in a sense, when she had saved his life.

'We were glad enough to come here at the time.'

Ilse snorted. 'Sometimes I think I would rather have burned.'

Babakov nodded. He had heard all this before. At the end of a particularly demanding day he had gone so far as to picture Ilse Lamprey as a bonfire. He had at once repented, for were they not all in this house (except for Miss Flitch) in the same boat? Shipwrecked, washed up by a dark wave on the same shore? They must hold together. In her own way it was Ilse who held them together.

'You will be expecting Professor Mowle tonight?'

'Damn the man. Is it Thursday? I suppose. Have we any sherry?'

'Only British. There is the apricot brandy from Christmas?'

'Sherry.'

Babakov looked out at the Convent. The lilac was almost in bloom. A quiet place, he imagined it, of gentle,modest women with soft laps. Virgins, of course, but in his day he had been a kind and appreciative taker of maidenheads. When Ilse was too much his soul strayed often there, grazing in the orchard among the novices. Yes, spring, he liked the English spring: the way it slipped in through winter's back-door, a shy girl with cold hands.

'We are fortunate, Ilse Lamprey.'
'You're an old fool.'

Fool? Yes, perhaps I am, thought Babakov back in his basement, leaving Ilse's Marmite cup for the moment on the slimy wooden draining-board, lowering his bulk gratefully into the big chair with the broken spring. The scent of his breakfast kipper welcomed him. Through the high window he could see roots, the earth that nourished them, the ankles of the young women on their way to or from Miss Flitch's tutorials. He had also noted the spot under the hydrangea Professor Mowle had given Ilse Lamprey where Elenora Flitch's Persians and his own little black secret cat did their business. Although this would undoubtedly be the death of the hydrangea, Babakov had not told Ilse who considered that cats should not exist in the first place but if they did they should not have bowels. A sudden unpleasant picture was presented to his mind: of himself, Babakov, serving Ilse Marmite in hell while she disembowelled an unending supply of Persian pussies.

While Dido and Aeneas tidied up their affairs at nose-level to his window, Babakov sighed, depressed by his vision. He was tired, he thought, he was tired to his soul which he saw as something like a ragged moth encaged in bone and too much watery flesh. The house was too big. He needed help around the place but Ilse would not hear of it. Elenora Flitch understood. He closed his eyes and remembered Elenora Flitch. This house is too big, Babakov, she said, you should have help. She laid her little white paw with the perfectly manicured nails on his hand (he could have kissed the spot) and offered him understanding from her wide grey eyes. Such a soft voice, such a curving smile, such a beautiful coil of hair that was for some reason prematurely grey. But she dressed to match it in toning English twin-sets and gently pleated skirts. Even her cats were grey. 'Come!' she would say when one knocked and

13

there she would be, in the dove-blue, high-backed chair, a cat on her shoulder, in an invisible cloud of lavender and roses. For Babakov, Elenora Flitch was pure soul. He could not imagine her going to the lavatory or taking lovers in the crude sense Ilse implied, though he permitted her from time to time a suitor. Elenora would be walking (barefoot? no – let her wear the softest grey kid-skin shoes, more of a slipper) across a dewy lawn. In a formal garden – such as he had seen at Hampton Court – she might stroll with a pale courtier in a maze, accept a rosebud, an avowal, a moth-like kiss on the hand or, just possibly, the cheek, before, with the puff of a sigh, dismissing the silly boy (who, Babakov most earnestly hoped, would then despatch himself tidily without blood, preferably in the artificial lake).

What all this boiled down to was that as far as Babakov was concerned, England was not food shortages and shocking weather and tired people, a peevish ex-Empress on a rainy day, but Elenora Flitch: *virgo semper intacta*.

Ah well, a man can still dream, take a nip of vodka, cook a kipper. Yes, just a nip from the half bottle Professor Mowle had slipped him on New Year's Eve. Babakov raised his glass: To the spring! To Elenora Flitch! To hope!

Twenty minutes later, Babakov was snoring, a sea-elephant in an armchair, gross, carbuncled, whiskered, beached.

In his small room at the back, young Janusz too nearly slept. Since he came to Ilse Lamprey's house he had hardly been able to keep awake long enough to open another tin of sardines or corned beef. He drank from the water-tap of the small hand-basin. His hair was starling-black, his face white. In his black trousers and white shirt he might have been taken for the waiter he had been. Among many things. A young, ill waiter waiting for a reason to wake, to unlock his door. Waiting for the English words to come to him so that he could unlock his door, walk out into England and say, hello, good morning, how are you, I am very well,

14

I like dogs, what is the name of your dog, do you think it will rain today?

Janusz had all these words in his head, from the second-hand book he had stolen soon after his arrival at Victoria, London. It was a book printed for the Free Poles in England during the war and the picture it gave of the country Janusz had regarded as a haven was both alarming and peculiar. So much weather! So many dogs! Also a darker world Janusz had not suspected (having failed to notice when the book was printed) of air-raid shelters and bombs falling from the sky. He was not sure at all, even if he could speak the words with which his head buzzed, that he wanted to leave his room to walk such perilous streets. He had understood the war to be over. Had another one started? Or had war drunk so much blood, grown so fat and hungry it had built its own kingdom in a world behind the world he could see from his narrow window? And any moment – while you were talking of dogs and weather – it might send a messenger to snatch you back?

It was very confusing. Not entirely for moral reasons, Janusz regretted that he had stolen the book from the same second-hand bookseller who had given him Ilse Lamprey's address.

He stretched out on his bed, his hands behind his head, his English phrase-book under the pillow, and wondered where was the England of Dickens? Where were the logs for the empty grate, the merry host, the coach-and-four, the famous fog?

Janusz sighed. On this side of the house where the sun never reached, he was unaware even of the spring. He closed his eyes. He concentrated his being into the only certain territory: his room. If he stayed very still, hardly breathed, he might be safe.

Yet he was a young man. Even here, even at this time in the century, even to his underfed frame, even in Radpole Road, something called, teased him, stirred his blood, made him turn in his sleep, whispered in his rather beautiful ear: awake!

The sun was as high in the sky as it gets at midday in spring in England. Babakov had left the window open. How tiresome. Spring breathed warmly in and Ilse Lamprey twitched her sharp nose in distaste. There, on the other side of the road, Mowle's silly wife, Valerie, was gardening, bent over a flowerbed (that'll get her rheumatism!), wearing what looked like an unbecoming cocktail dress, straw hat tied under her chin and gardening gloves. Dib dib, she went, dab dab. Coff coff, said that wretched old spaniel that should have been put down long ago. It was now staggering in circles attempting to bite its stumpy tail. Piles, without a doubt. Constipated. Poor Mowle.

Ilse reached for her list, added:

> Valerie Mowle
> Valerie Mowle's dog

In her room – quite the prettiest in the house since she had made it pretty – Elenora Flitch brushed an invisible butterfly from her smoke-grey skirt and considered how remarkable it was, the number of subjects one could entertain at the same time. Now, for instance, she was stroking Dido, paying proper attention to her pupil's essay, planning soft roes on toast for supper, wondering if she could afford that rather wonderful wisp of a chiffon dress in Colliers' window, and minutely rearranging her room. The primroses a little to the left, perhaps, the Botticelli Primavera face (not a bad print, such a modern face in a way, how sad Simonetta was dying already as she posed) reframed in olive wood and rehung at eye-level on her own side of the fireplace. Elenora always sat with her back to the light, whether she was teaching or entertaining. Kinder to the complexion and a hint of mystery perhaps? It was interesting about mystery, Elenora Flitch had found, a

16

matter mostly of emptying one's head entirely. Was that what men wanted? A blank page, an empty bowl? She had no idea. Men thought of Elenora Flitch all the time, but she thought very little of men.

Ah, the essay was finished. Elenora focused mistily on her pupil, Miss Posy Clamp (quite a good little figure but was acne really necessary nowadays?). Beta minus or plus?

'One must remember, of course, that the fourteenth century was an anxious age. Not unlike our own, in some respects. Yet it is interesting how romance is never quite put out. In a literary sense.'

Elenora's academic voice was soft and at the same time precise as she picked up her book and read:

> Nou sprinkes the sprai,
> Al for loue icche am so seek
> That slepen I ne mai

Elenora sighed. For what, wondered Posy Clamp who, like most of Miss Flitch's pupils was a little in love with her. That is, as a healthy girl in a university where men outnumbered women eight to one, she awaited true love with reasonable confidence, at the same time she dreamed of the day when her tutor, after such a sigh, would select Posy to whom to confess her secret life (perhaps a dry sherry, a Turkish cigarette?). That Miss Flitch was possessed of secret sorrows, Posy felt certain. A man killed in the war, most likely, to whom she had vowed to be ever faithful. Her hair had gone grey overnight at the news. She would never marry, never love again, but keep herself beautiful in respect for his memory. Everyone – it came to Posy – perhaps everyone, most particularly women, had one life they showed the world, another the world might never know.

Shutting the side door of Radpole Road behind her and stepping out into the spring, Posy glanced up at the small back window she had always taken to be a bathroom. Was that a figure looking out or a trick of the light?

She took off her gown, pushed it with her books into the bicycle basket and reflected as she rode that perhaps this was a funny in-between time in which they lived now. The war was well over and yet it wouldn't quite go away. There was Radpole Road where everyone seemed to be foreign except for Miss Flitch. There was never quite enough to eat at the hostel. Rhodes scholars from America handed out food parcels. Some of the men were old. If they hadn't been in the war, they had done National Service, in Germany or Korea.

Not that there wasn't fun. Posy was popular and there was always a party, usually a suitor at her heels. And that was the other in-between thing: you could never be quite sure nowadays when romance was going to turn into sex. Most of the girls Posy knew (and the men, for that matter) were virgins. They explored each other's bodies with interest and appreciation, they declared their love (in particular for Posy's small, high breasts), they sent flowers and notes and poetry. But more than once as she gasped in a punt or on a narrow afternoon bed Posy had been aware of the possibility and the peril of going too far. Had wanted to go too far. One day soon, Posy imagined, these things would be arranged, but meanwhile she did not want to get pregnant and she did not know how not to get pregnant. She was not even entirely certain of the facts of life. It really was an absurd situation to be in halfway through the twentieth century.

But Posy was of a sanguine nature. She took things as they came and dealt with them in that order. She also had a certain seriousness: most young people of this era in this place gave no thought at all to the times in which they lived.

Posy cycled on, contemplating romance and what exactly it could have been that made her tutor sigh. It seemed impossible to be so beautiful and have any troubles in the world at all.

What Elenora Flitch was actually sighing for was in part the chiffon dress in Colliers' window (a shade too blue?), in part the fourteenth century, which she saw as a perfectly dreadful time of disorder, plague and uncertainty – a bad time for poetry. No one at the moment was executing archbishops or marching on London but this decade was nevertheless another bad time. An unsafe time, at least, not as the war had been unsafe but in a different, nervous and glum kind of way, as though it were always winter.

And then there was something vaguely disturbing about the spring. There always was but this year it seemed sharper. Broken sleep. Odd dreams. Embarrassing fancies, as though something coarse had come to inhabit her, or something dangerous were approaching.

This would not do at all, Elenora decided. She would parcel out her day as usual in small packages. She would rearrange her room as she had planned, brush the cats, take a second look at that dress and after supper prepare her Chaucer seminar. Really, it was quite simple, after all.

By evening all was apparently as it should be in the area of Radpole Road and the Convent. In their cells behind the walls of the Little Flowers of St Anne the novices were making their small atonements for dancing in the orchard. There had been a dash of rain from the west, then something of a downpour. English weather. Night. Elenora Flitch was reading Chaucer, Janusz was awake, feeling neither happy nor unhappy, listening to the typical English rain. I am very well, it is raining, do you think the sun will shine tomorrow? The name of my dog is Rover. Babakov was filling Ilse Lamprey's hot-water bottle.

Ilse Lamprey had despatched poor Professor Mowle, after one glass of British sherry, to the dark, the rain, the night, Valerie Mowle, Valerie Mowle's toad-in-the-hole, Valerie Mowle's dog and Valerie Mowle's cold bed.

She herself had better things to do. She was writing the novel to astonish the world on the Olivetti portable donated by Mowle. With her list of dislikes beside her, she sat, but her head was empty, even of bread and butter puddings. She

19

felt absurdly sleepy. Could it be more difficult than she had imagined, to write a novel?

Then with two fingers she pecked at the keys and continued to peck. But what had she written? What was this? Or, more to the point, who was this?

Ilse had written: 'Out of the dark and the rain a shape forms. She is a girl with cold hands. She smells of ashes. Soon she will be here.'

With a snort Ilse pulled the paper from the typewriter and laid it face-down on the desk. There was a gap in the curtains. She twitched them to. She wheeled herself to the door and shouted: 'Babakov!' She tapped with her cane and called again. She felt cold. She wanted her Horlicks and her hot-water bottle. She wanted Babakov to put her to bed.

Ilse Lamprey called. No one heard.

Not Elenora Flitch who was sitting up in bed, wearing a powder-blue angora bedjacket, her long grey hair in a plait, reading *Troilus and Criseyde* and feeling rather peculiar, as though she were blushing somewhere low down, inside. Her nipples were hardening against her high-necked nightgown. She read:

> Hire armes smale, hire streghte bak and softe,
> His sydes longe, flesshly, smothe, and white
> He gan to stroke, and good thrift bad ful ofte
> Hire snowisshe throte, hire brestes rounde and lite.

Not Janusz, who was feeling suddenly and quite unaccountably happy. Who closed his eyes and dreamed that he was lying with a girl in a bed of lilac.

Not even Babakov heard. Hot-water bottle for Ilse Lamprey filled and abandoned to cool, he had felt himself suddenly overcome by fatigue and lay now, his bulk awkwardly spread in the armchair with the broken springs. His little black cat jumped on to his lap complaining, tapped his face with her paw, but Babakov slept on, mouth open, snoring, dreaming of Elenora Flitch's powder-blue bedjacket.

The Countess in the second-floor front did not hear either. She was watching with satisfaction as Gruber – a napkin tucked into his collar – picked up his chop and sucked the bone. The man who lived in the attic was, she supposed, slightly crude and had very little conversation. A snob too, apparently unaware that exiled Hungarian titles were definitely *déclassés* in post-war England. Never mind. If there were to be no more parties, it was something to have a good loin chop and someone to appreciate it.

She put on a record, sank down in her chair and closed her eyes. She danced in a hall of mirrors, there was a scent of gardenia, what a whirl, what a spin! Everything she had ever loved or been loved by was frozen in those mirrors. And how they played. Tara-dum. De-dum. Tara. Outside so cold, ice stars, deep black woods.

At least the music drowned the sound of Gruber's sucking. Would he dance? Could he dance? She doubted. The only music to which he responded like a soul in a coma half-waking, was Wagner. And who could dance to that? I ask you?

Miles and miles away from Radpole Road a slim figure, not much more than a shadow, was leaving Gottlieb's second-hand bookshop round the corner from Victoria Station. Although she must have come from the boat-train she had hardly any luggage at all and no one noticed her passage. The only person aware of her arrival in England was old Gottlieb himself and he had seen so many shadows in his time, there was no surprise at one more starveling ringing his bell after closing.

All the same, as he double-locked his door and turned to climb the stairs to his flat, Gottlieb's long nose twitched. He sniffed. What was that smell? Burning?

21

Chapter Two

Communities are frequently invisible. That is, no stranger, driving or even walking into the city by way of the northern suburbs would have been aware that this was a kind of village. That a web of sensibilities – intimacy, curiosity, passion, rage, love, passionate indifference – so fine you could not see it, so strong it could not be broken, was spread over 161 Radpole Road, over the home of Professor and Mrs Mowle and Mrs Mowle's dog and the Convent of the Little Flowers of St Anne.

And the web was not only strong but elastic. Posy Clamp, for instance, a mile and a half away in her college hostel, was aware from time to time of its pull. It was rather like a telephone call. She would be writing an essay, toasting a crumpet, yawning at Anglo-Saxon, kissing a boy, and her attention would be abruptly summoned to Elenora Flitch's room of sighs and secrets. Also, since her last tutorial, she had wondered more than once about the figure at what she had imagined to be the bathroom window.

Professor Gustavus Mowle too – a thin, uncoordinated, disorderly man, half-destroyed by his passion for Ilse Lamprey – would trail sticky threads of the web whenever he left the area of Radpole Road. Like an awkward bride he tripped on his train as he measured in jerky strides the two miles from home to college. He would look over his shoulder suddenly, a man transfixed – mowing down infants and dogs – as if Radpole Road might have uprooted itself to lumber after him: Ilse, with that delicious half-sneer, perched somewhere in the mid-air, Valerie and that dog he would like to garrot whizzing along on a detached piece of the lawn Gustavus had to mow every Sunday, waving handkerchiefs of complaint and shopping lists: Barko dogfood, rock salmon, Harpic, lavatory paper, Carter's Little Liver Pills and *Woman*. All the everyday discomforts of life. Somewhere, Gustavus thought, there must be another world where love, reciprocated, blazed, or one could, at least, have peace. Failing fulfilment, he would climb to his cold college room, sport his oak, light a Woodbine and be happy for a time in the company of wraiths – the celibates, the monkish clerkes who had occupied this cell in that other England, when all outside was darkness but here they toiled to keep alight a guttering candle in true and faithful hope of better days. Well, how else could one live?

Of course, this was a new village, an accidental village. They had all come from somewhere else, even the Little Flowers of St Anne, where on this morning – spring again after last night's rain – the gatehouse bell was ringing.

I suppose, thought Elenora Flitch, waking late from a very peculiar dream, pouring her pale straw-coloured tea into the milk-blue porcelain cup, drifting around her room, touching her favourite things, her talismans, I suppose I am the only English person in this house. Everyone else is a refugee and yet I feel at home here. I like it very much when I visit Mother Martin across the road (perhaps with today free, I might nip across: yes, that would be calming to sit beneath the lilac and take a tisane with Mother Martin, though she, of course, does not drink or eat in company, like the royal family who are never photographed conveying food or liquid to their mouths and never chewing, as if they lived on air like angels, even though it is perfectly clear that the Queen Mother has a weight problem). I went there in the first place in case I might discover that I had a calling. What a relief that might have been, how simplifying! But the truth was, I had to admit, I would have missed more than I realised from the ordinary world. Not just the

23

pusses but clothes, pretty things, my own room, the third programme, Middle English (I suppose they might have allowed me Middle English), dry sherry, Turkish cigarettes, the possibility, however remote, of something happening. What that something might be I have no idea. It may never come. But meanwhile 161 Radpole Road is a pleasant enough waiting-room. One could even live and die here. People die in worse places. The war is over but people are still dying in dreadful ways in terrible places.

Though I might not fancy myself as the Bride of Christ, I do not wait for a man, I insist. If there must be sex, let it be Milton's gaseous mingling of angel spirits. On that point I am certain. Anything else must be so messy. I will not allow mere dreams to plague me. In the common light of day, how pale they seem.

You could say that – in spite of that Lamprey woman – I fit into Radpole Road because I am, in my own way, another exile. That is, the country in which other people live horrifies me.

Ilse Lamprey is an evil woman. I know she spies on me but I rise above it. The new boy, Janusz, I have hardly seen. The Countess is quite nice.

I am restless this morning. I can't settle. I shall brush the cats. I shall not brush the cats. I shall not work on my Chaucer seminar, which in any case I could deliver standing upside-down with my head in a bag. I shall remember my good fortune to be living in comparative comfort in a safe and beautiful corner of an uncomfortable world, put on my brogues and go for a walk. The small fowl sing on the bough. Come on, Flitch – jolif and gay!

Elenora was not the only person in the area of Radpole Road who was restless that morning.

At the same moment that Posy Clamp, having decided not to do her *Beowulf* essay, nor to go to the Kardomah for coffee, nor to stay in bed, was mounting her bicycle and pedalling for no reason at all in the direction of Radpole

Road (passing Gustavus Mowle going the other way), in the second-floor back of number 161 Janusz was making up his mind to go out for the first time since he had arrived at Ilse Lamprey's house. With his cut-throat razor and the hard soap supplied by Ilse Lamprey, he shaved, nicking himself once but humming still as he read from the phrase-book propped up against the small mirror. He would have liked to have said: I am happy, I had a beautiful dream last night, will you dance with me? However, he would do the best he could with the words at his disposal and if no one understood him did it matter so much? He was alive. He was free. He rubbed the damp soap across the inside neck of his white shirt and scraped it off with the razor: a small improvement. He could do nothing about the trousers. Never mind. He was young. It was spring. He opened the door, made his way down the back stairs and found himself standing outside, in England, on the doorstep, looking at a girl with brown hair and small high breasts.

'Good morning,' he said, 'the weather is good. Do you think it will rain?'

'Hello,' she said, with the most beautiful smile Janusz had ever seen. 'You must be the new lodger. I'm Posy Clamp.'

Posy Clamp did not see Gustavus Mowle. Babakov, peering through the roots of the hydrangea, saw Posy's ankles and the worn tips of Janusz's small black shoes.

Ilse Lamprey saw Mowle (what a pathetic figure – hardly fit to be a victim), Posy arriving, and, through her opera-glasses Elenora Flitch in her grey Windsmoor skirt pause, as though uncertain, on the pavement outside 161 Radpole Road, then make up her mind, plunge down the path to the Convent. Not for the first time. Did they know, wondered Ilse, what a Jezebel they entertained? She considered a poison-pen letter but felt today unusually exhausted. Even wickedness might be too tiring. Even holding up the opera-glasses was too wearying, in spite of the fact that a pair of collar-doves were behaving quite badly in the Convent lilac and Valerie Mowle had not appeared at all today, with her dibber or her dog.

Babakov, Ilse said to the empty room. Babakov, she sighed, I am tired, so tired.

It was no wonder that Ilse Lamprey was tired. She, like everyone in her house but for Elenora Flitch, had come from so far and lived through so much. Have we not all eaten grass, thought Ilse, there is nothing so remarkable about that. It is understood that we do not speak of such times. She put on her black wig and was reminded by the card propped on her mantelpiece that the Countess was at home tomorrow. Silly old cow who thought she was still a girl at her first ball, or that was how she behaved, holding out to be kissed the very hand that prepared goulash of tinned meat for Gruber in the attic who pretended to be starving but could perfectly well have paid for his own meals at the British Restaurant. And Babakov, after a double sweet sherry, would tell them all how he had been brought up at Yanovka, on the German side of the ravine from Lev Davidovich Bronstein. Trotsky to you and me. And we all know what happened to him.

One had been young indeed, but it was best to forget it, Ilse considered, bearing in mind the flames that cut off those times like an infernal hedge. No going back, she had resolved. We must orphan ourselves, we must come from nowhere, we must make ourselves in our own image, we must be strong!

Ilse took a spoonful of Marmite. To punish Babakov for forgetting to put her to bed so that she had had to use those dreadful pulleys, Ilse had sent him downstairs and up again to fetch the pot. If one cannot rely on people one must be prepared. Babakov was careless, allowing himself to get old, there was no knowing when he might take it into his head to pop off. He would simply stop breathing without any thought for anyone else (and after all they had been through).

Ah, what they had been through indeed. Those last terrible days she had resolved to forget had turned her into a carnivore. She and Babakov had lived – once the cats and dogs and horses ran out – largely on grass, the occasional turnip, raw potato and puddles. And all the time, Ilse had dreamed first of steaks and chops then of whole animals: porkers with their throats slit, raw unborn lamb, giant cattle jointed to eat with one's fingers, like lobsters. She had dreamed of tankards, buckets, baths of blood. In those days she would have swallowed whole even Valerie Mowle's dog, mangy fur, rheumy eyes and all.

Her stomach, alas, had shrunk and never quite grown again while her digestion had been left an impaired and pathetic sort of thing requiring humouring and given to tantrums. Hence the Marmite. Even so, when Babakov could get it, she ate her liver raw, minced very small.

Ilse licked the spoon and, feeling better (that is to say, nosey and uncharitable) took up her opera-glasses. At the Convent the gatehouse bell was ringing and something interesting was going on. A small van had drawn up and two men were carrying something quite large inside. Roughly the size and shape, Ilse judged, of a small coffin. Heavy enough though for the men to be admitted. Ilse supposed there was not the slightest hope that they might rape and pillage the nuns. This was England, where excess rarely took place before lunch. Something to do with opening hours, no doubt. At night after closing-time, she understood, men of the lower orders would roll home to commit incest, kill their babies and chop up their wives into small pieces before burying them in their horrid little gardens. Only the aristocracy who drank sherry at eleven went to the gun-room to shoot off their own heads at midday (his Lordship said he was cleaning his gun, m'lud).

Nothing sensational was going to happen. The men must have been in the Convent for fifteen minutes before driving away: hardly long enough for a scandal. So the Little Flowers were still intact. Many nuns had degrees nowadays, Ilse was led to believe. There was even one, with a man's name, pebble glasses and black boots, who left the Convent from time to time for a tutorial with Elenora Flitch. Well, what do you expect of Anglicans?

Ilse put down her opera-glasses, wheeled herself to her desk, re-read that scrap of nonsense her typewriter had turned out last night, crumpled it into a ball and, on second thoughts, tore it into shreds. Great mistake, writing at night. One was open to any kind of fancy that cared to barge in. She put on her spectacles, addressed her list, and wrote:

> virgins
> secrets
> surprises
> blancmange
> The Countess
> The Countess's parties
> rock salmon

Not good enough. Could I be losing my venom? A second list, perhaps. Mowle had said that writers should ask questions even if they didn't know the answers, in the hope that in writing they might arrive at the answers. Very well.

> what is going on at the Convent?
> where is Valerie Mowle?

Ilse would have been disappointed if she had known where Valerie Mowle was: at her kitchen table with her hair in curling rags, drinking Camp coffee and smoking a Park Drive cigarette. She would go into the garden soon but for the moment, well into her third phantom pregnancy, she found herself increasingly lethargic in the mornings. And there was a very nice article in her magazine about the preparations for the Coronation, along with pictures of the new Queen ever since she was a baby. Valerie would always think of Her as Lilibet and only she, who entertained Her in her dreams, knew of the private joys and sorrows beneath the public face. My dear Valerie – Lilibet would say, sitting at this very table (such a delight to be informal!) – only to you can I confess what a burden is the crown. I see you too are a dog-lover (in dreams Cuff was still the young and bounding dog Valerie had first loved and always would, dying for the Queen, catching biscuits in mid-air, shaking paws – no sad ageing dribble of urine, no death). Would it surprise you to know that I Myself apply the corgis' flea-powder? That when I carry through my often wearisome duties I am in my secret heart, a horse? Shall I tell you my dream? (Here She would lay one royal hand upon Valerie's.) To put on my old tweed skirt, wellies, and retire to a stud farm! Ah well. At least here I can be Myself. Bless you, my dear friend.

Valerie sighed and leafed again through the pictures of her friend who was really little more than a girl: in pantomime at Windsor Castle, in her ATS uniform, on honeymoon at Broadlands, at Treetops, still a Princess, stepping down from the plane a Queen, dark-veiled at the funeral. At heart, just another housewife and mother like herself, yet now She was to be the hope of England. No one else could carry the sceptre and the orb, and She was not one like her uncle to lay them down. And heaven knows, we need some hope, don't we, Cuffy. All those foreigners across the road. Sometimes I wonder who won the war.

Well, we all have our bit to do. Come on, Cuffy, we must hoe our row!

If Ilse were a bat – which she might well have been (hanging upside-down in the corner of Valerie Mowle's kitchen) – she would have been bored. Her worst suspicion – that there was nothing remotely interesting about Valerie – would have been confirmed.

As an ugly black bird with manic eye and ragged wings,

huddled on a branch by the ferry at the end of the path that connected Radpole Road with the river, she would have been furious to see her new lodger in company with Elenora Flitch's pupil.

If not exactly happy (the agonies of spring and sex), Janusz and Posy Clamp seemed pleased with each other. They sat side by side in the lap of a great willow.

'How is your dog?' said Janusz.

'I thought I saw you at the window the other day. That is, I saw someone at the window, so I suppose it must have been you. Have you been in England long?'

Each was conscious that their hands nearly touched but not quite. Posy imagined lying down, this pale young man with the beautiful mouth bending to kiss her. He was like no man she had met before. Even those shiny black trousers suited him – she couldn't imagine him in brown corduroy. How splendid he would look in white tie and tails.

Birdsong was all around them. A small, exhausted brown duck was in splashing flight up-river from a gang of lustful drakes. The first punt of the season to find its way so far upstream was poled past.

Janusz imagined lowering Posy to the ground and bending to kiss her, smelling her hair, undoing perhaps the top button of her sensible English shirt. Instead he sat up straight, pressed his knees together and gazed sternly at the river. He had been brought up strictly in the Polish Corridor.

'The sun is shining,' he said.

Oh dear, Posy thought, this is going to be sticky. She liked kissing but she also appreciated conversation, letters, poems, telephone calls. At least until she had made up her mind how far to go and then it wouldn't matter, she supposed.

But then perhaps we do all talk too much. If you look at it from another point of view, words can be very confusing. Because they are often beautiful and we have so many of them and although they are very powerful they have no will of their own, we can use them without permission – wildly, madly – and get into terrible muddles.

At last Janusz turned to her and, taking one hand, kissed it. It's too late anyway, Posy thought, I'm already in a muddle. I think I'm in love.

'I must have been asleep,' said Ilse aloud. 'I dreamed I was a crow. Or was it a bat? Why are you smiling, Babakov?'

At the window Babakov was watching Posy and Janusz making their way, hand in hand, up the path from the river under the heavy blossom. It was his duty, he knew, to report this development but he had no intention of doing so.

'It is a beautiful day.' And there was Elenora Flitch walking in that brisk divine English way back from the Convent to 161. She carried a bunch of lilac. She looked up. She saw him! She waved! Turning his back to Ilse, Babakov made a small circling motion with his hand. He could always say he was cleaning the window. 'Perhaps you would like me to carry you out of doors, into the garden?' Perhaps in the garden under the spell of spring, Ilse would fall asleep after her bad night and perhaps Elenora Flitch would come out and perhaps they would stroll around the garden together and perhaps she would stumble and he would support her and she would rest her head on his shoulder, just for a moment. Perhaps one night the house would catch fire and he would break down Elenora Flitch's door and, holding her cats to her powder-blue angora bosom (Babakov had seen her bedjacket on the line), she would fall, half-fainting into his arms. (And where in this vision was Ilse? Burning in her wheelchair on the first floor? Tapping her cane in vain, for no one heard her. What's all this then, the English copper would say, covering his nose with a large white handkerchief, for there would be a stench like the ovens of Auschwitz. And nothing remained but the ribs of the wheelchair and a charred black wig.)

Elenora had disappeared indoors to her ground-floor flat from which escape in the case of fire would surely be easy. Life was very pale beside dreams, thought Babakov. Unlike Ilse he could still appreciate the everyday but his best times were in daydream or, better still, sleep, when he could shake off the infirmities that bound him increasingly and with one leap be free to wander in space and history, keep in fantasy the company he chose. In this dimension there was, in a sense, no history, no rough hand to force you from the room of youth, private hopes, small joys, when everything seemed possible.

Was that it? Was that the secret? To retain a sense of the possibility of the improbable? Even in these old bones?

So sharp and clear had been Babakov's vision, he half-expected to turn round and find Ilse Lamprey in flames (it was astonishing – considering she had saved his life – how often he imagined her crackling in hell). But he repented. She was looking impatient as usual but also tired. The spring was not kind to her. She was brave. She had been beautiful. Like him, she had simply entered history at the wrong time through the wrong door.

He said gently: 'You have not forgotten the Countess tomorrow?'

'I have not forgotten.'

'I could make your excuses?'

Was Ilse in a dream too? She seemed far away. But not for long.

'Excuses? There are no excuses. Ever. For anything.'

'Excuse me.'

The thin girl who had rung Gottlieb's bell in the rain, who had been hardly more than a shadow, was taking shape. She had spent the night on a bench at Paddington Station where in the first light of dawn she could have been mistaken for a folded mackintosh. But a commercial traveller had bought her breakfast in the station buffet and by the time she emerged she looked if not solid, at least opaque.

'Excuse me,' she said to the commercial traveller, who was rubbing his leg against hers under the table, just like a man-dog. The cleaner was still at work, the buffet was nearly empty, so she was noticed. If she had walked out into London and committed a crime, witnesses would have described a young female person with narrow pointed features, wearing a grey hooded cloak in some kind of material resembling blanket. The commercial traveller, an habitual bigamist, might have observed that she had deep-set eyes. She carried no luggage.

The Countess hummed to Workers' Playtime and now and then took a little dance step as she prepared for her At Home. Of all the exiles, Olga Rákosfalvi had probably adapted best to life in post-war England. Expecting snoek and spivs and smog, she had been quite pleasantly surprised by 161 Radpole Road. That first winter had been cold, certainly, but she had come from a colder place. There was something to be said for a small room, after all, if one wore one's wolf-skin, boots and the balaclava from the WI jumble sale. Also newspaper between good pre-war Jaeger vest and outer garments.

And looking on the bright side – as she invariably did – at least no one was likely to break down one's door in the night, she had a ration book and an arrangement with the butcher involving diamonds. Just as well she had as there was poor old rationless Gruber to look after since he would not look after himself. Not that Olga minded. In the past, the dancing time, she had been the one who was looked after, as if she hadn't a brain. Then the divine but rather stupid Max had shot off the top of his head when he heard the Russians were coming. And everyone else had gone away. So now, no longer cherished, exiled and obliged to use her own brains, Olga had turned herself into a more than competent housewife. She had her bad days, her mourning, when ragged birds cried Woe! and time seemed infinitely empty, a vast plain to be crossed with death at the end. Still, Olga had a gift for what other people would see as the trivial but was truly a rare joy in the immediate. She knew this to be a house of dreams and fantasy and forgetting and so, with her strong and healthy instinct for sanity, attached herself to that which could be touched, seen, tasted, smelled. A bright morning. A twig of blossom Babakov had brought her. The ghost of a chilly smile from Gruber. A small bottle of cheap scent. A bargain at the butchers. Babakov's information that the new young man at the back had been seen in the company of a pupil of Miss Flitch's, who must be invited to accompany him to her At Home. She would slip a card under his door.

Regarding herself in the brown-pocked wardrobe mirror, Olga thought it was just as well Max could not see her now – an odd woman dressed in a patchwork skirt cobbled from an old quilt, a tattered shawl over a sequinned blouse. Oh well, for fifty her figure was still not bad at all. Even Max would have found her small feet unchanged, the bosoms that had seemed top-heavy in her youth now appropriately ample. She had had to sell her yards of beautiful hair and she feared it was growing in grey but she was pleased enough with her ingenious arrangement of knotted scarves in jewel-bright colours.

Perhaps she just had time to try that purple lipstick she had found in the dustbin when she was disposing of Gruber's sucked bones? Apparently not. A thump above her head indicated that the man in the attic wanted his lunch. Potato soup with herring heads and a nice fat pork bone. He did like his pork, did Gruber.

Chapter Three

*T*he thin girl had a name now. Vera. She had tried it on. Sucked it like a sweet. It would do as well as any other name. Better than some.

It might even have been her real name. She had tried to remember if she had ever been christened, if she had a given name. She had very little memory and no luggage but for a generous pouch inside her cloak which contained, among other items, a small, indistinct photograph, a folded paper – a letter perhaps, a few dried crusts of bread and a couple of cooked sausages she had pinched from the plate of the commercial traveller at Paddington while he was trying to behave like a dog with her leg. There was also the address she had got from Gottlieb of Victoria.

Now Vera had breakfast and a name she took on a new decisiveness. She no longer felt quite so evanescent. She had spoken to people and been understood, she had food in her pouch and a destination.

The only problem was how to get there. Money was needed, Vera would get it. She was pleased to find that she was a strong-minded and practical young woman. Followed by the commercial traveller, she walked briskly from the station and after only a couple of hours in the shadows under the viaduct her pouch was crackling and clinking with money. On an impulse she entered a cinema and slept through most of the programme, waking to see a newsreel of a plump young woman wearing a headscarf tied under the chin, talking to a horse. In the seat beside her, a man in a raincoat was apparently excited by the film of the woman and the horse. His eyes were on the screen but his hand was advancing on Vera's knee. Her opinion of England sank again. She gave him a crack on the shin with the side of her foot and left the cinema.

London was beautiful now, dusky, bomb-sites veiled, budding trees sketched against elegant squares and an indigo sky. No one gave her a second glance though it is true that cats stiffened and swore, and evening dogs out for a stroll yelped in her wake.

Chapter Four

'*H*ave you a name for her?'
    'Shadow.'
'Very nice.'

161 Radpole Road was part of an organism but it also had its own nervous system. If Gruber were to scream in the attic Babakov in the basement would twitch in his sleep and the little black cat dozing on his chest would grumble.

Not at the moment, however, for Shadow was most comfortably resting on the only lap she would accept apart from Babakov's: Elenora's. It was not particularly ample but very soft and Elenora's voice was the kind that cats prefer: low-pitched and even. Also, she did not stroke you or pick you up without invitation, and knew the exact spot under the chin to rub with the ball of her thumb in one direction only.

In fact, Babakov thought, Elenora's voice was not unlike the purr of a discreet cat. As he sat regarding her with round eyes of pleasure, a dim but wonderful shape through his pebble lenses, he saw her for a visionary moment with small pointed ears, sky-grey fur and a languorous tail that would require brushing once a month. And he would feed her from her own Ruskin-blue dish nothing but the choicest rabbit, diced chicken, boned salmon and chopped liver. (In his dream-life such delicacies would be easily obtainable.) Mentally, he crossed off chopped liver. It reminded him of Ilse.

'I'm so sorry. What did you say?'

'I was saying you are the kind of person of whom people take advantage.'

37

Babakov pulled his nose and blushed. He was surprised he had enough blood left in him to blush. He had thought he was all water.

'You know of whom I am speaking?'

He nodded and just managed to whisper: 'I owe Ilse Lamprey a great deal.'

Elenora sat very straight in the chair with the broken spring. She spoke gravely, almost severely.

'There comes a point when debts are paid. You must think of yourself, Babakov. Have you ever thought of leaving Radpole Road?'

'Oh no! No, I couldn't do that. I don't see how I could.'

Suddenly he was so alarmed he forgot Elenora. His hand shook, rheum came to his eyes at the thought of packing his cardboard suitcase, shutting the door of his basement behind him and stumbling out, purblind, into a strange country. It was spring now, a queen was to be crowned, there must be hope, but Babakov could never quite forget his arrival here seven or so years ago, the view from the train of a country that was supposed to have won the war but looked more as though it had lost. Smoke in the ruins. A pall of brick dust. The terrible familiar intimacy of front-less houses like faces with their eyelids torn off. The sight had so affected him that at the moment of his salvation he gazed in horror and wished he could still weep.

By contrast, Radpole Road was heaven itself. It was a body into which he had wedged his weary soul.

'You see, I feel safe here.'

Elenora regarded him. It was quite difficult to be English at the moment unless, like her, you were fortunately placed. It must be frightful to be foreign. Now and then, when she allowed her mind to wander and was feeling not quite up to scratch, she would glimpse, as though through a torn curtain, a world gone under to a new dark age; death, the only free man, feasting among the ruins. There were drawbacks to being a medievalist. You understood, while handing out Chaucer in cheerful parcels, the precariousness of life.

38

'I do see.'

She did not say, I am not sure that anywhere is altogether safe. The short view is to be preferred. I have felt rather funny this spring. Quite carnal. Early menopause?

Well, one must pull oneself together.

'We're all in the same boat, at least.'

'Oh yes.'

The cat plopped to the floor. Creakingly Babakov stood. He almost forgot to open the door for Elenora. He was in the same boat with her. It was sinking. She could not swim. Her life depended on him. He struck out bravely for the shore.

It was true they were all in the same boat. That is, this was a house of lonely people yet the very fact that they were all in the same boat meant that no one was ever quite alone. They could lock their doors, pull Ilse's ratty eiderdowns over their heads, but there would still be a gargling from the waterpipes, indicating that someone was trying to get clean in the single claw-footed rust-stained monster of a bath, fed by a trickle from a dodgy geyser (baths 3s. 6d. by arrangement from six to seven p.m.). The experience was always gritty since under Ilse's instruction Babakov cleaned the bath with Harpic: a cut-price job lot Ilse had obtained through a contact in army surplus from whom she also purchased her coarse blankets and soap. (Elenora made her own arrangements regarding soap and thanks to Father Clement of St Jude's, the Little Flowers of St Anne, who gave her the freedom of their bathroom, enjoyed the best of modern plumbing; a worldly luxury perhaps but as Mother Martin said, times were changing and it would be a stodgy old church that did not move with them – there was even talk from America of giving up the habit.) The Countess complained of a rash, Babakov suggested Vim, but Ilse would not be moved. Those wretched creatures Gottlieb sent her were certainly infested. Harpic killed all known germs. She shut her mouth like a steel trap. Babakov nodded wearily and failed to suppress the image of Ilse in jackboots at Himmler's right hand.

So in Radpole Road there were always signs of life, comings and goings, paths crossing, the sound of Ilse's cane, the thump, drag and squeak of Babakov climbing the stairs, the nocturnal tramping of the man in the attic. Elenora visited Babakov, Babakov would find an excuse to visit the Countess with whom he felt comfortable, or Elenora, with whom he felt uncomfortable but ecstatic. No one visited Gruber, though he visited the Countess every day for his lunch, settling at her card-table and tucking a napkin under his chin (at first it had been newspaper) in hope, Olga guessed, of pork.

More than once, especially lately, Olga Rákosfalvi waited until he had sucked his bone then served his junket and said: 'You really should get out. To the garden at least. The spring is beautiful.'

His voice, rarely used, was rusty and faint. He mopped his grey moustache before speaking, leaving beads of fat. His skin had the most unhealthy pallor of dead meat.

'I am well enough here.'

'You need something to do. Every man does. There is plenty of weeding at this time of year.'

But it was always the same. He turned on her those fearful sunken eyes and she was silenced, reminded of horrors she thought she had forgotten.

Nonsense! Fancies. People are people. He is a man who needs feeding, no more, no less. If he has no papers, well who has in this house?

Thus the house lived. At times it seemed to breathe. It was protean. It changed shape according to your point of view. On a wild night in winter Valerie Mowle got up for a nice cup of tea, twitched open the curtain and saw a wicked hulk bearing down on her waving gnarled and hungry arms. For her husband Gustavus the Victorian turret and twiddles (even one false battlement) were on a moony night the castellations that held Ilse Lamprey, his princess, his untouchable love. (What he would do were she one day to whip off her knickers with a welcoming grin, he had never considered.) For the Countess, it was simply a smaller home than usual, somewhere to hang her pinny. She was not a woman given to fantasy but she did think that when she had prepared for one of her At Homes – prettied up her room with a bright shawl on the bed, a bunch of Innocence stolen from the garden by Babakov and stuck in a milk bottle, blue crepe paper on the card-table – the house approved. It grew warmer, kinder. It stopped gargling and whispering and squeaking and settled on its haunches waiting for the party to begin. Which would be soon. Tonight.

'There's a party tonight. This is a card inviting me to go with you. Isn't that kind.'

Posy, since she was underneath Janusz at the time, had seen the slip of white card pushed under the door, gently excused herself and returned to the bed where Janusz continued his shy investigation of her breasts. If the awful bed in the mean little room had not yet quite become a bower of bliss, it was still a very happy place to be.

Posy had tried sitting on the edge at first (well, there was nowhere else to sit except for the floor). Her intention had been to give Janusz his first English lesson and for a while he had been a model pupil. That is, he listened and repeated after her what Posy had said. She had finally discovered where he got all this stuff about weather and dogs and air-raid shelters and sat up late when she should have been doing her Anglo-Saxon grammar for a test tomorrow, drawing up a more practical vocabulary. The whole thing was turning out more complicated than she expected – rather like life. I mean, for instance, did you believe Evelyn Home or the Metaphysical poets? Well, the last, obviously, if you were an educated young woman living in the dawn of a new Elizabethan age. All that fuss about virginity was rot. Yet if Evelyn Home was wrong, Marvell wasn't exactly helpful about how the whole thing

41

worked. Someone in the hostel had got hold of the *Kama Sutra* and there had been many late-night study sessions but all had agreed it was like a course in Cordon Bleu before you'd learned to boil an egg.

Posy had arrived quite determined.

She sat up very straight.

'Good morning,' she said.

And Janusz replied, 'God mawning.'

'Good afternoon.'

'God afteroon.'

Had he shifted a degree closer? It was a very short bed.

'My name is Janusz.'

'Yez.'

'No. Not yes. You say: my name is Janusz.'

Was the room getting hotter? Why was it so difficult to breathe?

'My nome iz Janusz.'

Pale, long fingers. Her top button was undone.

Posy was a determined young woman, one of a sturdy generation. She had been nourished on swedes, war-time, dried egg and rosehip syrup. Then why was she shaking?

'Please may I have a cup of tea?' she read.

She was blushing from the roots of her hair to the tips of her toes.

'Can you tell me the time of the next train?'

Two buttons. Three. Well, yes, it would be much easier to lie down but, on the other hand . . .

'Here is my ration book. Janusz, are you really paying attention?'

Perhaps she should have asked Miss Flitch how to teach English? How to be English. How to be a woman. How to be graceful and beautiful and absolutely untouchable. Her tutor, on the divine plane on which she lived, Posy thought, would never have got herself in such a muddling situation. Just as her head touched the pillow she saw Elenora sitting on a cloud in one of the dim corners of the room, dressed in blue, hands folded, and speaking Middle

42

English. Her expression was one of mingled understanding and reproach.

'I do not speak English,' gasped Posy, 'please tell me slowly. Oh, Janusz!'

The Countess put the card under the door just as Janusz had unbared both of Posy's perfect little breasts. Posy slipped from under him and by the time she returned to the bed, he had to some degree collected himself. He would never have behaved like this in the Polish Corridor, but then he had never wanted to, since the cousin to whom he had been promised at the age of twelve had a face like a plate, an incipient moustache from the age of fourteen and no breasts to speak of. His clearest memory of summer evenings when he should have been swimming with the other boys or spying on the naughty girls or stealing fruit, was of walking Wanda. Go wash your face, put on a clean collar and walk Wanda, his mother would say in the same tone of voice she told him to walk the dog when it was on heat and had to be led, for reasons he did not entirely grasp. So he would cross the orchard between the two houses, kicking a tree on the way, and collect Wanda, who would be waiting for him with a scowl and a plait sticking out each side of her head.

Really it was Wanda who walked him, grabbing one hand in an iron grip and marching him up the hill, past the church and the barn to visit her aunt, who was a larger version of Wanda herself. The two would sit down in the parlour with the stuffed cat and the sepia photograph of the aunt's husband (died young) and discuss Janusz as if he were not there.

'He is too thin. We must make him some potato cakes.'

'What a funny little husband.'

Janusz did not feel like a husband at all. He wondered glumly if Wanda were planning not to marry him but to eat him. And it got worse. On her fifteenth birthday Wanda did not proceed straight up the hill. She pulled him into the barn and made him lie on a bale of hay while she climbed on

43

top of him. The hay made him sneeze and the weight of Wanda was squeezing the breath out of his body. At that exact moment, the first of September, German tanks were crossing the Polish border simultaneously from the West and the East, folding up the famous corridor between them. So Janusz was not quite squashed because his mother sent his younger brother to fetch him and then everything changed.

Janusz wanted to tell Posy all this but all he could do was kiss each bosom and tuck it up. Perhaps he wanted to tell her how guilty he had felt all the way to Gdynia and a corner in the hold of the last Swedish ship out (which put him ashore most unfortunately at Murmansk), thinking of Wanda whom he had not loved, whom no one but a wild Russian rapist could have fancied; who haunted him still in his sleep when those he had truly loved – his mother, his brother, his sisters – had lost their voices, gone like blind moths into the darkness. He had never quite been able to shake off that unlived life.

'Janusz.' Posy sat up. Since this was her country it seemed to her she had a responsibility to pull herself together. 'I think I ought to tell you, I am a virgin.' Janusz looked even paler than usual. Was it true that men led on and then frustrated got ill? Might even go mad? Was he mad? Damn. Where was the dictionary? 'I'd really better go. I'll come back for the party tonight. Janusz? Janusz, do you understand anything I say?'

He too was standing. He took her face in his hands then, as she was about to speak, put a finger to her lips.

'Beautiful,' he said. 'God afteroon.'

Mostly one was alone. Then suddenly the room was full of people. So many even Olga's housewifely instincts were stretched to the limit. She took a deep breath and touched her heart, wondering if the punch would do and if only there were caviar, silly old Max at her shoulder, a bell to ring. It was odd how one felt in company most alone.

'Please. Do sit down. Anywhere.'

'Well, I haven't much choice, have I?'

Ilse Lamprey indicated that Babakov who was panting heavily should put her down before he dropped her. Olga, arranging the cushions at her landlady's back, noted that Ilse looked tired, that her wig was a little askew as was the plum, nearly black lipstick – as if someone had jogged her arm while she was applying it. But the long skirt from which her legs stuck out like sticks was good-quality real velvet. It had been the star of Colliers' curtain display all winter. Not for the first time Olga wondered how Ilse managed so wonderfully. Ah well, it was not her business.

Just the three of them seemed to fill the room to bursting. Olga fussed with drinks and hoped the party would begin. In the wardrobe she had two plates of marinaded rock salmon on water biscuits. Should she produce them now? No. Wait for the others.

Ilse's eyes snapped. 'Such pretty flowers, Olga Rákosfalvi. Innocence?'

'Oh yes, aren't they nice – so fresh. Now I have a surprise for you tonight. Ah! Here they are. Our new young friend, Janusz, and I fear I didn't catch your name, my dear? And here's Miss Flitch!'

Ilse looked at the Woolworth's glass of dubious liquid and shuddered, mentally adding to her list: Olga Rákosfalvi's punch.

'Can we expect Dr Gruber tonight?'

'Oh, I do hope so! I tried to make him promise but you know how shy he is. Was that the bell? Ah, Professor, there you are. *Entrez!*'

Whatever was in the punch (nettles, Algerian red, a bottle of Ilse's gin Babakov had misappropriated from the locked cupboard in the scullery, the Countess's potato vodka, Merrydown cider and something else), the taste was not altogether appalling and the effect was striking.

'Grzyb,' said Janusz, kissing first Olga's hand, then Ilse's, then Elenora's.

45

'I'm so sorry?' said Elenora.

'Grzyb.'

Olga had forgotten to take off her pinny. She had forgotten, mercifully perhaps, to serve the marinaded rock salmon on water biscuits. Gustavus Mowle was trying to explain the Marian cult in Poland, which explained all that hand-kissing. Babakov, who had been serving the drink from a soup ladle, sank down on the other side of Elenora Flitch, who was wearing a divine sprigged lawn dress and a little blue eye-shadow, and told her how he had been brought up at Yanovka, on the German side of the ravine from Lev Davidovich Bronstein. 'Ah,' he said, 'such days,' and a tear plopped from his eyes. 'On our side we had the fat cows. For them, the lean.' Elenora waited for him to go on but was distracted by the thin, pale disorganised man with sprigs of cotton wool on his cheek where he had cut himself shaving. So far as she could understand, Gustavus Mowle had stopped talking about the cult of the Virgin Mary in Poland and was positively ranting about the dawn of spring in medieval literature in a way Elenora in other circumstances (was the room rather hot?) would have put down sharpish as unscholarly. At the moment, however, she did not feel up to the *querelle du Roman de la Rose*. She was feeling, in fact, a little mad and was just on the point of asking if her colleague found Chaucer erotic. Then she realised suddenly that if she were not, thank God, English, she might have fallen that moment, as if enchanted, fearfully in love or more precisely into lust with this chaotic fellow who sat with his pointed knees tucked under his chin. Ilse Lamprey unknowing (or possibly knowing all) rescued Elenora from flinging Gustavus to the small square of floor remaining and tearing off his awful clothes. Metaphysically.

Ilse was saying there had been something funny going on at the Convent yesterday. What is happening to me, thought Elenora? Am I become as mad as them? They? Could he be Abelard to my Heloïse? Love and destroy me? Or simply, at least, change his wardrobe.

'Oh no. It was just a television set.'

'A what?'

'Father Clement of St Jude's. I think he hired it. So that they can see the Coronation.'

Ilse had hoped for a body or a rape at least. Still, a television set was interesting. She would have to think about that. Write to the Pope? Oh no, of course. They were under the Archbishop. Anglican. Even so, should they not have renounced worldly goods? Or if the television set was rented, did that not count?

She lit one of her thin black cigarettes in the amber holder and surveyed the cramped party with the most enjoyable distaste. The Flitch woman was quite flushed and her hair was coming down. Since Ilse cut him off, Mowle, who had been on the edge of making a fool of himself, had abruptly stopped talking at all, like a wireless switched off. The Janusz boy and the pupil of Elenora Flitch's were sitting hand-in-hand like a pair of bookends with nothing between them (lovers? She'd have to put a stop to that) while Babakov told them about living in the Ukraine on the other side of the ravine from Lev Davidovich Bronstein. So long as that was all he told them. Ilse had nightmares sometimes about the secret she shared with Babakov. It was getting dark. The garden was filling with shadows. Surely that was a human form crouching just outside the loom of light from the window? Ilse shuddered. It was alarming to reflect what the world would give for their secret. And on the other hand, delicious.

Someone said: murder.

'Oh yes,' said Olga Rákosfalvi, 'it was in the evening paper. Quite awful. Poor man.'

Ilse was alert again. Nostrils sharp. Nerves keen.

'What man? Where?'

'A commercial traveller. Paddington. Slain, it said, and apparently without motive. A motiveless killing. Father of five.'

What could this mean to Ilse? Nothing. Yet she felt as if

47

someone had left the door open and she sat, abandoned, in a bitter wind. Wolves howled. She was a bundle of bones in a city of rats. Any moment the walls of Radpole Road would dissolve. One's hold on life was so brittle, easily snapped. Pouff! You're broken, gone. Ashes. Scattered.

'I remember,' said Ilse, hardly aware that she had spoken or that the room had fallen silent. 'I remember *die Stunde Null* – hour zero. Berlin. The whole of that great city fallen silent. At night you could hear only the gnawing of rats. And the elephant. Babakov? Are you there? You remember the elephant? The last in the zoo. And the stink, of course. That is something you never forget.'

Babakov wagged his big head. Ilse, a tiny bundled shape propped against cushions, spoke out of the darkness.

'You see, there were no coffins. You have to understand that. Food, we thought all the time of food: squirrel, jackdaw, raven. And dandelions, you remember, against the hunger-typhus. Of course, we did better than most, the three of us. We had gold. I remember exactly where we found you, Babakov – on the subway track from the station below the Wilhelmsplatz! With our gold and your legs we did well enough. Those bloody Russians never found us and it was a warm winter. Never got us, did they?'

Babakov was grinning and thumping his knees with his hands.

'A close shave once or twice, Ilse Lamprey. But they never found us!'

'History is a fool. It knows nothing. We escaped history. People do, you know. Except there is always memory. If I could, I would make a hole in my head and tear it out. That is the most terrible thing of all. To remember.'

Abruptly, Ilse seemed to come to herself, to awake. What had happened? She must have drunk more of that poisonous concoction than she realised.

'Babakov. Time to go home.'

'But my dear Ilse Lamprey!' Olga protested. 'Dr Gruber will be so disappointed.'

48

'Babakov!'

Ilse was frightened of being alone. Of the figures in the garden. She straightened her wig. Old witch. Nothing left to you but spleen. And terror.

Motiveless killing.

'Rubbish!'

'I'm sorry, Ilse Lamprey. What did you say?'

It was dark. Babakov was half-oceans over. He had nearly dropped her on the way downstairs.

'There is always a motive. For everything. Babakov?'

'Yes?'

'I want to go to the lavatory. Turn on the light.'

Janusz wanted to turn off the light.

'No. Honestly. I forgot to sign out. Oh dear, you don't understand, do you? That drink was frightfully strong but you see, if I'm late back I get gated. I do love you though. I just have to work things out in my head. Perhaps if I learned Polish? No, Janusz, please! I'm very confused. I've never met anyone like you before. No, really, I'm going. Sorry. It was a lovely party and you looked so handsome. I just wish I could explain. I want to kiss you and kiss you and stop talking. And kiss you.'

Posy cycled back to her hostel under a gibbous moon, wobbling a little from Olga's concoction but mostly from her desire to lie down underneath Janusz and stop thinking.

The moon saw everything and understood nothing.

Olga wishing Max were here or even Gruber. The pleasure of any party was talking about it afterwards. And there were the canapés, still in the wardrobe! The water biscuits had gone soggy but the marinaded rock salmon might do for Gruber tomorrow. She cleared up steadily, methodically, not altogether sadly, until the room was her own again and she could pat the cushions straight and let the smoke out of the window. Rooms had lives. They

49

needed to be visited. Well, there would be plenty to think about now, for a week or two.

Also under the moon, the form Ilse had seen in the garden was on the move, creeping closer to the house in the direction of Elenora Flitch's lighted window on the ground floor: a clumsy and amorphous shape followed by a wheezing animal: a familiar?

'Cuffy dear, please try to be quiet!'

In flannel nightie, cardigan and wellies, Valerie Mowle – who was supposed to be at home in bed with her hair in curling rags, drinking Ovaltine and looking after her third phantom pregnancy – raised herself until her nose was level with the crack in Elenora's curtain. Gustavus, she had guessed for a long time, was up to something. Well, men always were, weren't they and she had not really been bothered until lately when quite suddenly, in the middle of bedding out her salvia, a most lurid picture had come to her mind of her husband making passionate love to another woman. She had suspected that foreign woman in the wheelchair so what she saw now surprised her so much she fell back into the flowerbed. With the greatest difficulty – since Cuffy was trying to lick her face – she righted herself and waddled as fast as she could on all fours across the lawn. And under the rhododendron collided with another quadruped.

What Valerie saw was Elenora Flitch sitting in her powder-blue chair with Gustavus on his knees before her.

'Professor Mowle! Please!'

Elenora had never before seen anyone actually wring their hands.

'Miss Flitch! Elenora! That woman has nearly destroyed me.'

Surely he couldn't mean that odd fat creature who did his gardening?

'I haven't actually met your wife.'

'Not Valerie! That damned Ilse Lamprey.'

'Oh dear, surely, it can't be as bad as that?'

Had he guessed? Had he sensed what queer feelings visited her tonight?

Elenora tried to talk sensibly but she felt as though she had a temperature. Even cradling his grizzled head on her lap, mentally she lay already beside him in her virgin bed. Where were the pusses? Where the still, guardian soul, robed in grey, who had kept her all these years from muddle?

'Coffee,' she whispered. 'And then you must go.'

More or less sobered, sat on the rosewood rocker, Gustavus had the air of a saint, Sebastian perhaps, afflicted by arrows. She wanted very simply to take him and to comfort him. But nothing was ever so simple.

'I really don't believe that one person can destroy another, though admittedly I have little experience of such things. Ilse Lamprey is a forceful personality but what hold could she possibly have on you?'

Gustavus groaned. He put his head in his hands.

'She has stolen my soul.'

'Oh come!' Even as she spoke, Elenora wondered. A few hours ago she would have had no idea what Gustavus was talking about. Now she had a most uncomfortable feeling that she did understand. 'You are speaking metaphorically, of course.' She found it difficult to swallow, as if she had a fish-head stuck in her throat. 'I take it you are in love with Ilse Lamprey?'

'I am devoured!'

'I don't know very much about love. I have been thinking. Do you find Chaucer erotic? I'd never thought about it before and I've been teaching him for years. I could give a Chaucer seminar in hell. You know, I'd never considered that either? The matter of hell. Except as the absence of heaven. Now I wonder. And now you really must go.'

Gustavus had probably heard not a word she said but the

tone of Elenora's voice had soothed him remarkably. Here in this room of pale tones and quietness, it was like sitting in church. This was the first woman he had ever met who could keep still.

'Of course, you are above all this. You are a remarkable woman, Miss Flitch.'

'Elenora.'

She walked out with him into the garden. The air was black and sweet, the moon sticky silver, the philadelphus shone. Elenora prayed that Gustavus would seize her by the shoulders, fling her down upon the grass (would it be damp?) and possess her. And prayed that he would not. So was left with her soul and her body detached one from the other, as he shook her hand and shambled off into the night. Her soul was glad to see him go and suggested a nice cup of tea and just this once, perhaps, a sleeping pill. Her body – in particular the erogenous zones – reminded her that she lived on a temporary concession in a world that passeth soon as floures faire. So make hay.

Little did Gustavus know, as he dislodged the snoring Cuffy and stretched out his long white body in his marital bed, that Valerie had had her own drama that night. As though the scene she had witnessed through Elenora's window were not enough, there had been this other animal on all fours obstructing her waddling passage out of the garden. Valerie had barely stifled a scream, when the other thing squealed instead. Gallant Cuffy – with a rush of remembered youth and vigour to his head – had sunk his few remaining teeth into the bulky dark-blue shape. Ten minutes later, after hissed reproach and apology on both sides, Detective Sergeant Rainbird, CID, was having a nice cup of Ovaltine at Valerie's kitchen table while she mended the torn sleeve of his navy raincoat. He fancied flannel (something to do with an all too distant childhood trauma) and found Valerie, even – or especially – in the circumstances, a fine figure of a woman. The war had overlooked Rainbird (flat feet) and so had the peace (no promotion). Life, really, had overlooked him, when he came to think of it. His fantasy had been modest – to come home to a warm kitchen and a woman in flannel – and though he knew he could stay only as long as it took to patch up his coat and drink his Ovaltine, he could not help dreaming that this was his life, this his woman. There was, of course, that bloody dog now chewing its stump of a tail in its basket. Well, one thing at a time. He gave it six months at the most.

'Nice dog you've got there.'

There was cunning in Rainbird's small eyes.

'Oh! Dear Cuffy. Yes, he is my only friend.' Almost, Valerie added to herself, wondering if her small adventures would be of any interest to her one true Friend who had said only yesterday, sitting at this very table sipping just a spot of Gustavus's Tio Pepe from the college cellars, my dear, I have been selfish, you hardly speak of yourself. But then, though She hid it well, She was clearly anxious that We had finally agreed that the ceremony would be shown on television. One is, after all, an emblem, One belongs to the people, and I'm sure Mr Dimbleby will do it very well but One is also a private person, my-husband-and-I. No, no more, thank you. I do believe I have lost a little weight, don't you? Mr Hartnell will be pleased.

'A lovely home,' said Rainbird.

'Thank you. There we are!'

'Almost invisible.'

Valerie looked round, alarmed. The problem with Lilibet was that sometimes She was just half there while the rest of Her was involved with public duties of which there were so many at the moment.

'The mend.'

'Oh yes. Well.'

'Hubby home soon?'

'I expect.'

'You'll be wondering what I was up to.'

53

'Yes?'

'All I can say is that if I could tell all, you might be surprised.'

Valerie was suddenly aware that she was entertaining a total stranger, a man at that, she wearing her flannel nightie and a cardigan. She had taken off her boots.

'I expect you have your job to do like the rest of us.'

Rainbird buckled up his mac and put his finger on the side of his nose.

'Anything you see. Glad of a report. Over the road. We all remember the Fifth Column. Enough said?'

'Indeed.'

Rainbird paused, agonisingly halfway through the door. Mentally Valerie had already washed his Ovaltine mug, turned out the lights and gone to bed where Gustavus unsuspecting would find her snoring.

Rainbird shut the door but left one foot inside.

'Not at liberty. But let me give you my card. Any time. Night or day.'

'Certainly.'

Even when the door was closed his voice stayed in the kitchen like the smell of fat after frying.

'What I say is, who won the war?'

Chapter Five

*V*era supposed a new-born child must feel something like this. Astonished by almost everything. Ravenous. Outraged. Plonked down without a by-your-leave in a world that appeared to be completely insane.

Scraps of memory were returning to her. Most of them she did not like very much. A few, connected with the slip of paper carrying the Radpole Road address, interested her enough to get her back to Paddington and on to the train. The suburbs folded away behind her, she dozed and woke in a rural England of bright green fields, blossom, and black and white cows. She took a sausage from the pouch of her cloak and swallowed it whole. She was beginning to enjoy herself.

After the Countess's rather peculiar party, Radpole Road had taken half a day to pull itself together. To Babakov's relief, Ilse Lamprey remembered nothing. Janusz Grzyb was too young to have a hangover. He took Posy's *Winnie the Pooh* down to the river and, sitting under the willows, wrote on the fly-leaf: Posy. Posy Clamp. Posy Grzyb. Tomorrow he would learn English. He would read this book about bears. He would get a job as a waiter. Tomorrow.

Today, Elenora Flitch, after a lie-in and two aspirin, was doing *The Romaunt of the Rose* with Sister Michael, who would certainly, Elenora thought not very kindly, get a first. With black boots, pebble spectacles and a moustache. Really, she wondered, why did someone like Sister Michael bother to be a woman at all?

Elenora struggled not to give her essay an alpha. *Hard is the hert that loveth nought/ In May, whan al this mirth is wrought.* What could this creature in boots understand about heart or mirth or May?

'Yes, of course, on the one hand the convention of courtly love as expressed by Guillaume, on the other, Jean de Meun's biting satire.'

Elenora was finding it hard to keep her eyes open. Such a heaviness in the air. Was that the door-bell? 'So where would you say that Chaucer stands in his attitude to the *Roman*?' I am losing my edge, thought Elenora. I am becoming woolly. I had never realised before how well Chaucer understood the body. And the soul.

'It is a little hot. Perhaps, Sister Michael, you would be good enough to open the window?'

Ilse slept with the window closed. The sun did not find her out.

The Countess was out, coaxing bones from the butcher.

Gruber was in his attic, counting dead and money. He scratched his grey stubble. He was lonely and afraid. Only two appetites remained to him: hunger and rage.

It was Babakov who at last awoke, groaned, buttoned up his fly and stumbled to answer the bell. His first impression was of a nun or a ghost, then he saw it was a thin girl in a grey hooded cloak. For a shadow, she seemed sure enough of herself.

'Gottlieb sent me. Is this the right address?'

'You'd better come in.'

Just a girl, he thought. Like the rest of them, half-starved. He waved her towards the basement and shut the door behind him.

Then Vera fainted.

Chapter Six

*I*f a nation can be said to have a soul, England's – officially at least – was perking up. The old man who had won the war was back as Prime Minister. Lean, hard men, one of whom would later turn into a woman, were walking up Everest. There was a great deal of talk about a New Elizabethan age as if suddenly something were going to happen on June 2nd and everyone would be different.

Ilse Lamprey sniffed and wondered aloud how an English Archbishop proposed to turn a plump mother of two into a virgin. That would have been a challenge even for the Pope of Rome.

Both Gustavus Mowle and Elenora Flitch were co-opted on to the University Coronation committee, which had been meeting for six months and reached no conclusion about the appropriate way for such an ancient foundation to mark the occasion. There were those who believed that the occasion should not be marked at all. The People – that is, the Town as distinct from the Gown – might have their street parties if they wished, with tea from urns and beer and paper hats and children being sick, but for the university, what was one more Queen? They had seen so many come and go. Another block was in favour of fireworks. Another for Morris dancers and ringing of bells. A pageant? A masque?

'Miss Flitch?'

'I'm sorry?'

The room was stale with words. So many words, so

much talk. Elenora had a headache. She had a fantasy. Just lately she had been from time to time alarmed at the ease with which her mind nipped from her body and passed uncalled-for remarks or behaved in ways fantastic and sometimes actually wanton. At this second she was imagining simultaneously what it would be like to nuzzle that delicious spot where the nape of Gustavus's neck met his collar and how nice it would be to stop all talk in this city of talk. Scatter all those words of the ages like a cloud of gnats: all that Latin, French, Old French, dead Greek, Old Icelandic, Old Scandinavian, Anglo-Saxon, Middle English.

Middle English? Elenora woke up and realised that every face at the oval table was turned in her direction. She heard herself speak.

'I think a medieval fair.'

From when had these almost corporeal fancies (in the sense that Elenora not only thought them but saw them, as if looking through a window at herself behaving badly) begun to trouble her? She could not quite give a date to their metamorphosis into moving pictures, but it was surely only recently that she had felt herself losing the capacity to control them, to pull herself together? This morning, for instance, as she made her way through St Jude's cloisters to the committee room, she could have sworn that a particularly hideous gargoyle, with devilish wings, had winked at her.

And now, as she spoke, she was mentally undressing the chairman (a senior fellow of All Hallows, no less, and a world authority on some subject that at the moment slipped her mind).

The chairman spoke. Normally he could not tolerate females but he had always permitted a soft spot for Elenora. She was pleasant to look at without issuing any of those embarrassing sexual challenges. She had a soft, low voice. She did not nag. She did not weep.

'A first-class idea, Miss Flitch.'

Off with that daft hair-piece (whom did he think he was fooling?). Come on, strip down. Jacket off, waistcoat, tie, shirt, braces, trousers. Now then, dearie, don't be coy. What's under those knickers, then? Oh, you poor little soul, just as I thought. What could you do with that?

'Miss Flitch?'

'I'm sorry?'

'Yes, it is a little hot. Perhaps we could break there? A sub-committee? Time of the essence. If we are all agreed?'

Elenora walked round the quadrangle with Gustavus.

'Well, that's settled at last. Your idea went down very well.'

'What? Oh. Yes.'

'Parting of the ways.'

They were at the porter's lodge. Elenora seized Gustavus by the shoulders and flung him to the ground. Those awful corduroys! Let me release you!

Gustavus was still upright.

'I'll walk you to the bus. Are you going back to Radpole Road?'

'Yes. I suppose so.'

'I'm glad you have help there now.'

A hand under her elbow to steer her across the road. Could this be orgasm?

'I'm sorry. A little dizzy.'

'What's-her-name?'

'Vera. Oh yes. She's a great help. I don't know how we'd manage without her. I suppose we did but now she's here it's as though she always had been.'

Queens and great ladies envied me my joys and my bed.

Poor Heloïse. He never really loved her. But at least they had bed. Was that enough, Elenora pondered, as she was carried into the northern suburb where the chestnuts hung terribly suggestively heavy? From the top deck she could

59

see over the Convent wall into the garden she had thought once might restore her to innocence and peace. How she yearned for it. How distant it seemed. And yet not impossible. Was that her soul: the worn white cloth flapping reproachfully on the line between the chapel wall and the quince?

(Actually, within the Convent, Mother Martin was watching *I Love Lucy* on the coffin-shaped television set upon which she, the sisters and the novices were to view the Coronation of the head of their Church. Meanwhile she was utterly absorbed. A brisk Englishwoman who had never considered herself naive and in another life would have had her hair permed every three months and shopped at Jaeger, Mother Martin was astonished by what she saw. She had heard of television, of course, but this was the nearest she had been in her life to a miracle. She must check with Father Clement if watching too much television might be a venial sin. Nothing to burn in hell for. But Purgatory? Perhaps?)

Gustavus was right. Vera had made all the difference to Radpole Road.

When Babakov opened the door and Vera fainted, the Countess, back from the butcher, had dropped her bag of bones, caught her, put her to bed and when she came to, fed her from a spoon with cow's heel soup and semolina. Before her very gazé the poor child seemed to put on flesh. There was something odd about her eyes but otherwise she was just another perfectly ordinary person who had taken the underground route via Gottlieb of Victoria to Radpole Road.

Like everyone else she had dreams.

The second thing she said – after introducing herself at the front door and then fainting – was: 'Where am I? Am I in hell?'

Olga clucked.

'There dear. Have a little nap. You'll feel better. Poor child, she's having nightmares.'

After some difficulty in getting her down the stairs they had settled Vera in Babakov's lumpy bed. Time enough to tell Ilse Lamprey.

Babakov grunted and pulled his bottom lip.

'I suppose if hell is to be found on earth there is no reason it should not be at 161 Radpole Road.'

'My dear Babakov! You know quite well that hell exists only if we allow it to.'

'Yes, of course,' he said. Olga always cheered him up. She was a comfort – a comfortable woman for a Countess. Though his dreams were of an unattainable Elenora Flitch, Babakov's daytime fancies turned now and then to an easing picture of Olga sitting on the other side of an ample hearth knitting one of those eccentric collections of coloured squares she made from oddments of bring-and-buy wool at the church hall. Olga standing at his mother's kitchen table in the Ukraine, making dumplings. Even Olga lying beside him quietly on a feather bed – company in which to grow ripely old.

How many lives we live, thought Babakov. We are in the same flick of a second old and young and dying, dreaming and living. We are born and like a candle we are snuffed out. Not, after all, on the Wilhelmsplatz subway track where he had seen death (nothing much, after all: a wavering figure as grey as Elenora's angora, that soothed the hunger cramps then ducked and dissolved before an approaching lamp and his astonishing resurrection). But any time now, in sleep, at the corner of the stairs to Ilse's room.

But what is wonderful – how many lives one frame, breathing in and out for so many years, can hold. The worked-for, the dreamed of, the realised, the wished-for. And the here and now, which was lying at this moment on his bed between himself and Olga.

'She looks better already. But her hair. Had you noticed?

61

It's white. Yet she has a young face. I don't think we should question her. Let her take her time,' Olga whispered.

'Ilse Lamprey will have to be told.'

'What is it? What is going on? Something has happened and no one has told me. I have said, Babakov, I will not have secrets in this house.'

Wigless, bald, Ilse woke from her wild, poisoned sleep and sat up in bed with the affronted air of a fledgling buzzard. Her stomach cried for raw meat it could not take and her mind was a muddle of pictures and talk and awful drink and shadows in a dark garden. And something about a body. Then a blank. A darkness. Sleep. More like death.

Well, Ilse was very much alive now. She woke with a snap, certain only that something she had expected had come to pass. Arrived.

'Babakov! Pass me my wig.'

The third thing Vera had said was to Ilse Lamprey.

She had woken up feeling much better and fatter, accepted a bath and tied a large white handkerchief of Babakov's around her hair. She looked almost normal, if a little like a nurse. She was probably the only person on earth who was not frightened of Ilse Lamprey. All the same, it was true that Vera had no ration book.

'I can cook and clean though.'

'Yes? I suppose you look sensible. And we could do with the help. Where do you come from?'

'I don't remember.'

'Just as well, I daresay. There is far too much remembering. It would have been interesting to hear news of Germany, all the same. They are saying that things are quite comfortable there now, but that is propaganda. Is your amnesia total?'

'Almost.'

If Vera's response was a little too quick, Ilse did not notice. To her surprise, she was quite enjoying herself. She

62

suspected this child would not be bullied. It was a novel experience.

'Why do you wear that cloak? You're not by any chance a nun?'

'Oh no. It's all I have.'

'We must get you an overall of some kind. The Countess will know. We have quite enough nuns already. I can't abide them. You will find this a strange country where hardly anything is as it seems and no one says what they mean. Have you read *Alice in Wonderland*? A pity. It's a helpful book when coming to grips with the British. Now I'm tired. You must go. Babakov will tell you your duties and find you a room. There is a little one left in the basement next door to the pantry. No view, but I daresay that doesn't bother you. There are a few rules. About baths. And Dr Gruber in the attic doesn't like to be bothered. Not that anyone would want to. He's the dullest man I've ever known.'

Ilse waved her hand in dismissal.

'Off you run then. I have work to do.'

When Vera had left Ilse sat for a moment. Then she wheeled herself to her desk and laid out her lists like playing cards before her on the green baize surface. She felt a little breathless as if, on leaving, the girl had sucked the air from the room. Have I made a mistake, wondered Ilse? Could she be a deep breather? There is also a draught.

To her list of questions she added:

> does Babakov have a secret cat?
> is Vera a virgin?

But her heart – if she had a heart at all – was not in it today. Even her malice did not surge as vigorously as usual. Small nesting birds with boring English brown feathers were shrieking in the drainpipe but Ilse could not be bothered to bang on the window, to imagine the crunch of those tender bones.

That fool Babakov had left her a copy of *Britannia & Eve*, a hand-me-down from the Countess who should know better than to splash around her diamonds on such rubbish. Ilse flicked through the pages. Carrot mousse. Ragout of potatoes. Do-it-yourself Formica coffee table. Knit your own wedding dress. Paint one wall of your lounge purple. Dandelion salad is fun. Dear Anguished, your symptoms are unusual but I am sure if you consult your doctor he will set your mind at rest. Which twin has the Toni? Cauliflower soup serves eight. Bamboo screen room divider. Indoor plants need love. Crochet a Juliet cap. Ah! This was more interesting. She who wears the Crown is Britain's Hope. A deliciously disgusting double-page spread showing the overweight young mother of German extraction wearing a headscarf, kilt and Pringle twin-set alongside speculative sketches of her Coronation gown, some professional, a couple the results of a readers' competition, one of which featured sequinned leeks and the remarkable motif of a diamanté kangaroo.

Australia was something Ilse Lamprey had never got to grips with. Her interest was slipping. She yawned but read on all the same. An objective observer – as she saw herself – she was amazed that such a tired little country really believed that this fairly plain girl might put on the mystical robes of Gloriana and give everyone a second chance. Was there hope in the air? Did England's heart beat as one? Had she failed to detect it? Hardly likely, though disturbing all the same.

Ilse realised suddenly what was alarming her: the idea of change. Her life, the life of this house, depended almost literally upon the preservation of things as they were. If her visions, the shadows in the garden, ever took tangible shape, she feared for 161 Radpole Road.

Action was needed. Almost any action. She opened the drawer of her desk, took out one of the telegram forms she always kept handy, and wrote: GOTTLIEB ANTIQUARIAN VICTORIA STOP END STOP.

There would be no more ghostly exiles coming to Ilse's door.

There was nothing you could quite pin down but since Vera's arrival Radpole Road had definitely looked up. The protean house had awoken, flung open its windows, let in the sun. Vera was nowhere to be seen and everywhere, scouring with ammonia, clearing cupboards that had not been opened for a hundred years, washing, mending and re-hanging curtains. She continued to wear Babakov's white handkerchief, washed daily and knotted at the nape of her neck, and as her face filled out a little her nose appeared less pointed. On Ilse's instructions, Babakov had handed over his bunch of keys and every day one or other of the lodgers would be pleasantly surprised. Janusz came home from an English lesson with Posy by the river to find his army blanket covered with a cheerful red striped bedspread. (No one missed the runner from the dark passage to what had once been the flower room.) Elenora was surprised by a small, intensely sweet-smelling lily-like plant she had never seen before. (On her afternoon off Vera had exchanged her sensible housecoat for her grey cloak and paid a visit to the University Botanical Gardens.) The Countess was the startled and rapturous recipient of a bottle of Coty's 'Chypre' (an inappropriate and unwanted tribute from Gustavus that had been pushed to the back of Ilse's knicker-drawer and forgotten since a year last Christmas). To Babakov, Ilse also contributed, unknowing, the bottle of schnapps she had hidden somewhere she could never call to mind (the secret place beneath her mahogany commode) and a packet of her small black cigars.

There was no doubt, everyone agreed, that Vera was a treasure. A slightly stern one (strangely the cats seemed not to take to her at all), not given much to smiling or conversation, but she asked no more than her keep, 2s. 6d. pocket money a week and privacy (the little room by the pantry was always locked).

Her presence was at once all-pervading and almost invisible but if there was something odd about her, as the Countess said, we were all odd-bodies here and it is such a relief to have the bath cleaned with Chemico and the gritty bits at the bottom washed out. Even the taps shone.

'I do wonder if she eats enough. She looks well but I have never seen her take food to her room. Perhaps she has a snack in the kitchen. I must say she brought me a very nice little supper last night. It might have been rabbit. I wonder if Ilse Lamprey knows she is cooking. Is anything wrong, my dear?'

The Countess was in Elenora's sitting-room drinking mint tea. Elenora put down her cup untouched.

'Well, to tell you the truth, I have not been quite myself lately.'

Elenora sat in her dove-blue armchair, her small feet in the soft grey pumps crossed at the ankle.

'You're not worried about your beautiful cat?'

'Oh, I expect Dido will turn up. She never wanders far.' Elenora seemed to be struggling to make up her mind, though nowadays she could never be sure where her mind was or what it might come up with next. She had sat through the sub-committee on the medieval fair this morning and said not a word even though they were clearly getting the whole thing wrong. An academic out of his period is a lost child, she thought, as she listened vaguely to talk of fire-eaters, jongleurs and madrigals.

She would have to confide in someone and she had always found the Countess *sympathique* but the problem was, Elenora did not know exactly what it was she needed to confide. She could hardly speak of that awful coarse voice that lived inside her or her deep fear that one day soon it might persuade her to do something embarrassing. Of the idea that had come to her last night, like poison dripped into her ear as she lay awake in her sickly scented room, that if she were to do away with Ilse Lamprey she

66

might have Gustavus at last. Of her slapdash attitude to the work which had been for so long her life. (Yesterday she had given Sister Michael a gamma for a first-class essay on *The Legend of Good Women* and Posy Clamp an alpha for looking pretty.) Of the whiff she had scented under the lily-smell of something like burning. Of the miasma she had first observed this very day in a shoe shop, suspiring from the thick carpet they laid to make you feel comfortable in shoes that were at least a size too small, rising to her ankles. If she looked now it would probably have reached her waist.

Elenora would have liked to discuss the matter with Mother Martin but she had the terrible feeling that were she to put one foot inside the Convent, God would find her out and she would be as good as stripped naked for all to see.

'I've just been having some bad dreams lately. Silly to make a fuss. Perhaps you could tell me. Do you believe in hell?'

'Well, of course,' Olga said. 'For how otherwise would there be a heaven? It's really quite simple.'

Elenora nodded. 'I suppose it is. But if God created the earth and was pleased, whyever did he permit a hell?'

'How interesting. Babakov was saying something of the sort the other day. What I feel, my dear, is that there is fearful suffering and there is hell. They are not at all the same thing. We may suffer quite dreadfully and in our human weakness we may give the name of hell to our pain. When he gave us free will he granted us that right which you may see as a curse. I am a simple woman. Hell can wait. Heaven to me is here on earth.'

'I expect you're right. Thank you.'

Olga rose and smoothed her invisible apron.

'Tell me, do your symptoms worsen after midnight?'

'How did you know that?'

'Avoid cold, wet weather. Warm body. Cool head. And

Arsenicum Album three times between meals but not after toothpaste. It rarely fails for someone of your colouring.'

'Thank you. You've been very kind.'

Everything Olga Rákosfalvi said made sense in the light of common day. It was after dark that Reason like a sensible dog took to its basket and reality might be confused with phantasm and vice-versa.

Not that Detective Sergeant Rainbird, CID, held with phantasms. If the devil himself had shot up from the cells in a cloud of sulphur Rainbird would have taken his fingerprints and mother's maiden name.

As it was, he sat around midnight at his desk, catching up, as he put it to himself, on the paperwork; in fact, putting off as long as he could, his return to the bedsitter on the wrong side of town he could never bring himself to call home.

Sifting through the day's reports, messages and bulletins, he shifted his bulk in his chair and hoped, as always, that one great day (tonight perhaps?) these scraps of human folly and wickedness might add up to reveal the beautiful pattern of iniquity he was looking for.

Slowly and greedily he read. Rape. Lost dog. Unidentified torso, male. Female remains. Lost dog. Logged at two p.m. a call from Paddington Green police station regarding a body. Routine to all stations on Paddington line. Slain father of five bitten to death beneath viaduct is reported by Forensic as having scraps of some grey fabric beneath his fingernails. Re your query: Antiquarian bookseller of Austrian extraction arrested in Victoria for sale of pornographic literature. Investigation under way into illegal immigration of undesirable foreign nationals (copy to Interpol, Home Office and Foreign Office). Things were looking up. Rainbird licked the end of his pencil and in back-sloping writing continued his private notes on a certain house under observation in Radpole Road. When the time was ripe he would reveal all. Meanwhile it might be necessary to pay another visit to the desirable Mrs Mowle in her cosy kitchen. Thinking of steaming flannel, Rainbird slapped his hand. He must concentrate. There were connections, he felt sure, if only he could snuff them out. Something to shake the world and ensure him fame and a lifetime of Ovaltine and warm slippers. He knew it: the greatest villain of all time was so nearly within his grasp he felt quite dizzy. Hello, hello, he said to himself, rehearsing, I must ask you to accompany me to the police station.

And after dark, while the Countess slept the sleep of the kind, Janusz dreamed of English bears and Posy Clamp, Ilse groaned at the pain in her withered legs, Babakov snored and Elenora slumbered uneasily on the breast of phenobarbitone, Vera locked the door of the tiny room by the pantry behind her, slipped upstairs, three flights, and with her pass-key unlocked the door of the attic where old Gruber of the burning, hollow eyes, paced out the night.

Chapter Seven

*I*f you could only fold up darkness and put it away at the back of the airing cupboard.

If you could clear the cellar of history, dump it on the compost heap with the cabbage leaves and the eggshells and let it rot until it turned to brown gold for the rosebed.

Ilse Lamprey thought.

If you could take the ancient knowledge of this university, grind it small and produce one sausage of wisdom.

If you could kill with a glance.

If you could be born old, tired and disappointed and live until you were young.

If you did not have Gruber in the attic.

Then everything might be all right.

But people live their own small lives, regardless. Pluck flowers. Make burrows in ashes. Get born, crowned, buried. Pregnant, raped, burned.

Ilse looked out at the dash of rain. The tiles shone on Mowle's roof. English weather is like a slapdash house-wife, she thought, always wiping a wet grey cloth across grimy surfaces, never a clean sweep.

What is the matter with me? This morning Vera brought me a little minced liver, just right, so much more appetising than Babakov's messes. She stood at the window for a moment, the light on her face, and, I thought, she looks like someone I knew when I was young. No beauty, but not to be ignored. She'll get what she wants. I wanted her to stay. If she stayed any longer I might have told her everything.

I know her. I have the feeling that I recognise her. But when I asked her (what a risk to take): 'Were you ever at Obersalzberg?' she shook her head. 'I don't remember.' But in any case she'd have been too young.

What has happened since she came? The house is cleaner, but there is a change. I am an old woman afraid of the dark. I am sorry for myself. She has sucked out my rage.

Radpole Road had become like a patient with a temperature. Babakov, with more time on his hands now they had an efficient housekeeper, had downed the schnapps purloined by Vera and given himself up almost entirely to fantasy. Half-slumbering in his basement while Shadow mewed for food, he thought of hardly anything but Elenora Flitch. He looked up and there in the air between his chair and the mantelpiece was her curved smile. He blinked, smelled lavender and roses, twitched in his sleep as Shadow tapped his cheek with her paw, and woke to the certainty that Elenora's virginity was threatened. Throwing off Shadow he pushed himself to his feet. He must guard her. He must follow her. He must save her!

Even the Countess had a headache and since Vera's delicious rabbit the other night, quite severe indigestion. Neither of which were improved by the sight of Gruber pecking at his brawn (if anyone so lugubrious could be said to peck, which is on the whole a cheerful activity).

He groaned and pulled the napkin from his frayed collar. Olga forced herself to remember that he was just another soul – a very unhappy one – who needed feeding.

'Really, you must try to eat a little. A cow heel perhaps? I saw some rather delicious lights in the butcher's this morning. A morsel of tripe?' He shook his head, pushed back his chair and shuffled to the door. What was to be done with the man? 'Is something troubling you? To take away your appetite?'

At the door the old man turned. His gaze always

horrified Olga but it seemed different today. Was that fear she saw?

'Everyone is against me. The whole world. Even my own flesh. My trust has been misused by many people.'

The only ones unaffected by the atmosphere of Radpole Road were Janusz Grzyb and Posy Clamp. Or perhaps their fever for each other was already so strong they both had permanent temperatures.

Janusz read: 'Here is Edward Bear, coming downstairs now, bump, bump, bump.'

They were sitting side by side on Janusz's new bed-spread. It was too damp for their nest in the willows. Even though the sun was out now the weather had been bursting into tears on and off all day. Janusz's English was improving in an eclectic kind of way.

'What is this bear? Is he serious?'

'Well, sort of. Not really.'

Janusz shook his head and nibbled Posy's neck without using his teeth.

'I love you very much. Let us go into the bed.'

'*Please*, Janusz. If you are to get a job you must learn English.'

How could she explain, thought Posy, about the English and virginity, when she did not really understand herself. Everyone told you to keep it, but what for? Increasingly she saw it, embodied in the shape of a sensible English female, sitting firmly between herself and Janusz, making irrelevant conversation. She would have liked to discuss the matter with her moral tutor but Miss Flitch had been definitely rather odd lately, as if she were somewhere else. Posy felt she was reading the essays she wrote frantically now in half an hour with no preparation not to Miss Flitch but to Aeneas, wrapped like a stole round her tutor's shoulders. A cold critic.

'You see, everyone reads *Winnie the Pooh* when they are young.'

She felt short of breath. Janusz had undone her buttons and was looking at her breasts. She felt her breasts looking back with appreciation.

'Oh! So beautiful!'

Posy sat up straight, leaving Janusz panting and stranded and very confused.

'Janusz. Are you a virgin? Oh, hell, where's the dictionary?' Posy tried again. 'Have you got into bed with a girl?'

Janusz thought of Wanda in the Polish Corridor and shuddered. He shook his head.

'Oh dear. Then I do think we'd better wait. The trouble is I'm very ordinary. I had a happy childhood and I love my parents. I want to get a degree and I don't want to have a baby.'

'Yes! We make a baby!'

'No, Janusz darling. I don't think so. But I do love you. I'll find a way. Yes. Please kiss me again. Just there.'

For the first time in her life Posy had a sense of the landscape of her own body – hills, valleys, meadows, oceans – as a country it would be wonderful to explore with Janusz by her side. No – inside. And she knew with absolute certainty that somehow this summer she would.

The day after she visited Gruber in his attic and showed him a photograph, Vera put on her grey cloak and set off, walking from Radpole Road to town. She felt carefree for the first time for so long: the girl she was. Her memory had almost entirely returned. Early summer was thickening. She was no longer an orphan. She had her mind on shopping. She never saw the bulky shape following her. England was not so bad, she thought. It was simply a country that could not make up its mind which side it was on: life or death.

In fact there was something of a parade down Radpole Road that day. First Vera striding out, ignoring the bus-stop, then Rainbird, cramped from his observation post behind the Mowles' compost heap, where he had spent most of the morning. In agony he had observed Valerie hanging out her flannel nightie to dry (hubby would be eating breakfast in the kitchen that was rightly Rainbird's) and with some difficulty had repelled that bloody dog. Cuffy could hardly hear or see but he had snuffed out Rainbird all right. Foiled in his ambitious attempt to tear off both the Detective Sergeant's legs, he had barked hoarsely at the compost heap until Valerie Mowle called, pegs in her mouth, 'Cuffy, you dirty dog, come away from there!'

Rainbird, whose temper was short after a sleepless night and an unpleasant breakfast at the Odd Spot Café (bread bangers in thick skin, cold tea and a slice of cheek from that daft Linda who needed her bottom smacking hard with a shoe, preferably Rainbird's), bared his teeth and growled back at Cuffy, who retreated yelping through his catarrh.

Valerie embraced her dog. 'Poor Cuffy, did you see funny rabbits then? Or pussy cat?'

In pursuit of Vera, Rainbird crawled on his stomach from the compost heap, leaped the privet hedge and, limping, dodged his way crabwise down Radpole Road from tree to tree. Loping behind him, unaware, came Gustavus with lists in his head ('senna pods, dear, and suppositories for Cuffy and don't forget the mince'). After Gustavus, as Valerie Mowle watched from her washing-line, came Elenora, not at all sure where she was going, her hair not quite as tidy as usual. Really rather a mess, Valerie was pleased to see. Harlot. Wanton. Her hand trembled. After the scene she had witnessed the night of the Countess's party, she had been utterly confused. She had consulted every article on How to Keep Your Husband but could relate none to herself. Elenora Flitch was not in Valerie's eyes the Other Woman but a burglar. Which reminded her of the other odd sensation she had experienced lately: the impression that that large policeman whose eyebrows met in the middle was quite often somewhere around. What she would have done without her friend she could not imagine. Valerie had never intended to burden Her at such a busy time but dropping a stitch in the matinée jacket she was knitting for her phantom child, she had also shed a tear, and Lilibet had understood at once just as though she had told Her all.

'My dear friend, your problems are Ours. Frankly, We prefer dogs and I am sure that yours is a comfort.'

'But surely—' The first meeting between the young Princess – no more than thirteen – and the handsome young lieutenant. At Dartmouth. A true romance.

'Oh yes, indeed, Philip does look so good on a postage stamp. One does One's duty. I'm sure you understand. Well, I must slip off. Another fitting. If only I could stay! A problem shared is a problem halved, though that is a luxury I have rarely permitted Myself. Except in your company. Meanwhile have you thought of a hobby? I do recommend Lad'o'Mine for the 2.30 at Kempton. Just a little flutter? Why not?'

Valerie burst into tears.

And after Elenora came Babakov, even blinder than usual from the surprise of daylight and not quite certain what he was doing standing at the gates of 161, gazing after Elenora Flitch. Ilse rapped on the window. There was nothing that infernal woman didn't know.

Somewhere around Martyrs' Cross, Elenora had lost sight of Gustavus. What to do? Where to go? Go on, dearie, treat yourself, said the voice in her head and before she knew how it had happened she was in Colliers' lingerie looking at black underwear.

'Oh, Vera! What a nice surprise. Are you shopping? I was just looking. I can't think why. I never wear black. Underneath.'

Something about Vera made her shudder, but then none of her reactions at the moment were predictable. There seemed to be some kind of cloud around the girl that reminded Elenora of the miasma in the shoe shop.

The assistant was regarding Elenora impatiently.

'D'you think I should buy it? It's silly but I can't make up my mind.'

Vera said: 'I think people should do what they want to do.'

'Yes. Of course. You're right.'

Vera walked off briskly and in the cubicle Elenora hardly dared look at her reflection in black suspender belt, low-cut wired black brassière that did remarkable things to her breasts, and no knickers. Actually, there seemed to be two reflections. One was shocked. The other winked. Go on, ducks, it said.

After an awkward half hour in the ladies' dress department of Colliers', dodging behind pillars and very nearly arrested by the house detective, Rainbird, clutching a wrapped flannel vest ('a little something for the missis') slipped into the gents in the yard outside the Britannia to make up his notes. He sat in a stall on a closed lavatory seat, resisted with a struggle the urge to undo the flannel vest and wrote with his stubby pencil. At Colliers', Subject paid gold for dirndl skirt, Alice band and embroidered blouse.

He had to get a grip of himself. So near and yet so far. If he could make the connections, smoke the fox from the attic, he'd have his feet up in Mrs Mowle's kitchen for the rest of his life. Apple dumpling, steaming flannel, Golden Syrup pudding, spotted dick, toad-in-the-hole and a nice pair of buttocks, thank you. Steady lad! Plod's the word.

It had been a long way from the first scrap of paper found in the dustbin of 161 Radpole Road to the antiquarian bookseller of Austrian extraction, through newspaper files and back to Radpole Road. A few ripe plums – in particular, as the fruit of a little trip abroad carefully prepared for and planned, a copy of a letter preserved by his family from the papers of a certain Hieronymite Catholic priest, deceased.

Rainbird did not care for Abroad but any sacrifice was worth the prize. He who saved England from foreigners today. Tomorrow blacks?

Back at the station Rainbird was aware that he should put through a call to Paddington Green, knowing what he did about a grey, hooded cloak. Instead he buried his nose in reports. The usual domestics (if a husband doesn't have the right to chop up his wife in small pieces and flush her down the toilet, who does?). Spot of fuss with the university proctors about a chamberpot. The customary number of lost dogs (red collar, miniature, answers to Rover) but cats too this week who, not being licensed, were, as far as the police were concerned, legally vermin. All the same, someone's pet, Rainbird supposed. Bit odd that. Moggies could usually look after themselves. Nasty beasts. If he had his way they'd all be named and numbered and if necessary castrated. He sighed and tried to think of something to report. Soliciting at the Odd Spot Café? That would do. He typed out, one-fingered, an interesting memo that would put peroxide Linda behind bars for the rest of her natural, if he had his way.

A few more cats died that day. On respectable streets, sitting on walls, mats, in the shadow of the thickening summer, watching birds, sleeping, in alleys, suddenly. Crack went their spines.

In his attic Gruber studied a photograph he had thought he would never see again. It was hardly faded: a lovely blonde, so fresh, such a beautiful girl, snapped on a mountain walk, her face tipped to the sun, laughing for him. Perhaps he should have let her go to Wien? He had had evil counsel, even then.

Old Gruber wept: a strange sound, like a voice unused for a hundred years. He kissed the photograph and wept. The girl he had known so long ago: Geli. *Meine liebe Geli!*

Chapter Eight

*E*ngland was going through one of the periodic attacks of dottiness that seize her most often at times of disaster. Her boredom and tiredness since somewhat unrewarding victory had been relieved only momentarily by a revival of the Dunkirk spirit for those who danced doggedly in the rain at the not very festive Festival.

Now, for once, Britannia was anticipating orgasm for happier reasons. It was spring, a Queen was to be crowned, hope was in the air, the bird was on the bough and in Ilse Lamprey's drainpipe and, doubtless, nine months from June 2nd there would be a bumper crop of babies conceived on wet grass and a flood-tide of warm beer. Abandon panted offstage. Even Virginity, so long prized, stood poised and interestingly veiled, sucking her thumb and contemplating Lust with an expression that would have reminded Rainbird of lightly laced Linda from the Odd Spot Café.

Not even that house so wrapped in its own fevered dreams, 161 Radpole Road, could avoid the national fantasy. Like everyone else, they were circulated by the Town Coronation Committee and Ilse Lamprey, with only a small curl of the lip, agreed to a modest Union Flag provided it were no larger than five inches by ten and she were not required to pay for it.

Meanwhile, there was the promise of an interesting war between Town and Gown on the subject of St Jude's meadow, owned by the university but booked months ago by the Mayoral Committee for jollifications involving beer tents, outdoor dancing, biggest baby prizes, bonfires and fireworks.

Who had been responsible for the booking no one knew, though fingers were pointed at the Bursar who was at this moment enjoying a well-deserved sabbatical in one of the less pleasant South American countries. The university, in any case, was rarely troubled for long by anything resembling reality and the Coronation sub-committee was happily undergoing a parthenogenetic crisis: dividing, sub-dividing and dividing itself again. At some point to the medieval fair had been added an Elizabethan barge, floodlit with the coming of darkness to reveal no one less than Gloriana herself, appropriately attended, arriving by water.

Elenora, half-asleep in the amber dust of the ages, had been absently observing the flight of a honey-drunk bumble bee from the windowsill to the chairman's flies. She was mentally opening her mouth to say she had no knickers on when it struck her that she had been addressed and everyone was looking at her. Even nodding encouragement.

'Oh no. No, I really don't think so.'

'But you are perfect, Miss Flitch! Even the right profile.'

And a virgin to boot, she thought glumly.

'I'm really rather busy.' I've lost my cat, I'm out of my knickers and half out of my mind. Oh Gustavus, if you could see my black wired peephole bra! 'Surely – an undergraduate?'

The chairman winced. So far as he was concerned the *status pupillaris* should never have been extended to females who showed far too much leg on their bicycles and distracted his most promising students. What was needed here was a mature respectable woman who knew how not to behave like a woman, dressed in quiet colours and wore her skirts below her knees.

Thus the matter was settled. Elenora had been elected Gloriana.

*

'It's not even my period,' she protested to Gustavus Mowle over coffee at the Kardomah.

'I think you'll do it very well,' he said.

'*The Faerie Queene*, I suppose. It's years since I read Spenser.'

His hands were so long and white, his air so languid, he was a kind of divine wilted celery stick. And he was Ilse Lamprey's! Elenora groaned. Had they consummated their relationship? Elenora doubted it. Perhaps some arrangement might be made regarding body and soul? 'I'm sorry? What were you saying?'

'I could lend you a copy. *The Faerie Queene*.'

'Oh. Yes. Thank you.'

Everywhere Elenora looked there seemed to be couples: birds mating, dogs mounting bitches, even here, in the middle of the morning in the Kardomah, undergraduates pairing off, two by two. Come on, my lovely lad, get it out, give us a look. The warmth was rising from somewhere embarrassingly low down up to the roots of her hair.

'It's rather hot.'

'I say, isn't that the foreign girl from Radpole Road there with a boy? I must say, she's perked up.'

'Vera? Really? Yes. I'm sorry. I must go. I have to report a cat.'

Missing. One grey Persian cat. Dido. Miss E. Flitch, 161 Radpole Road.

Detective Sergeant Rainbird had spent most of the day following Subject wearing, he would have said, a sight too much make-up and not enough blouse for any decent female; she had been in and out of men's colleges like you-know-what, drawing upon the weary Rainbird the suspicions not only of a number of college porters but of young Bright who, new to the force and too true to his name, had attempted to apprehend Rainbird himself for loitering with intent.

Rainbird had his plans for Bright from which he was

diverted by the day's record of missing moggies. Dido, my angel! He took another bite of pickle sandwich and with the nearest he ever got to a grin, mentally inserted his foot in the front door of Radpole Road. From the front door to the attic a step or two. Ho ho, what have we here?

So intense was his excitement, Rainbird was obliged to turn his mind to something less tasty than his coming triumph. He settled on Valerie Mowle's bloody dog and a mile or so away Cuffy, peacefully biting his piles under the Mowles' kitchen table, let out a strangled yelp.

'Hush, Cuffy,' said Valerie. 'It's "Mrs Dale's Diary".' There were all sorts of things she should have been doing but just lately she was so up and down she was afraid if she did anything at all it might be something quite dreadful.

On the surface things were looking up. (Janusz and Posy wore the thick skin of innocence. In a way, they were outside this story, cuddled together in a punt beneath the willows.) Yet there was murder in the air as well as summer.

Valerie Mowle could have killed Elenora Flitch.

Elenora imagined tipping Ilse Lamprey out of her wheel-chair into a snake-pit.

Rainbird would have had Cuffy put down, painfully.

Vera was capable of killing anyone or anything. Perhaps she had already killed. For the moment though, she was finding the exercise of power more interesting. She knew who she was now. She knew where to go, how to dress to tempt the boys. She was fascinating. She was foreign. She was an irresistible and malevolent Zuleika Dobson who knew how to entrap and torment, where to bite and how. In three weeks, sixty undergraduates lost their virginity. Green boys, fresh and pimpled with the season, would have died for her. She would have let them. She imagined the crack of their bones. Meanwhile, she accepted their flowers and kisses and groans. She left them bruised.

'I hate men.'

Vera brought Ilse Lamprey her mid-morning bouillon.

81

Ilse nodded. 'I used to hate a lot of things. I can't quite remember what they were.' She pondered. 'Nuns, I think. And England.' She sipped her bouillon and looked up at Vera who, in Radpole Road, dressed down severely. 'Are you quite sure you were never in the Prinzregentenstrasse? Oh, of course, you have amnesia. How could you know.'

Was the girl trying to be friendly? Did she expect an answer? Mistily, Ilse thought that she had once had a role in mind for Vera, though exactly what it was she could not call to mind. An ally? Some kind of daughter?

'They only want one thing.'

'Yes, I do remember that.'

Vera was crushing a honey bee on the window between finger and thumb. For a second Ilse could have sworn she popped it in her mouth. She rather wished the girl would go away. She tried to remember what it was like before she came.

'Perhaps you would be good enough to send Babakov up? I have hardly seen him lately.'

'He has a secret cat.'

Vera's smile was a little weird too. She appeared to close her mouth but you could still see her small, sharp teeth.

'I thought so.'

'I had a mother. I know that.'

'So did we all, I daresay.'

Ilse handed back her bowl and spoon. The Marmite had been particularly tasty today. Something extra. Only when Vera had left did Ilse recognise the aftertaste. Surely not. Blood?

The more Vera perked up, it seemed, the lower sank old Gruber. The Countess worried. Black pudding? Just a teeny spot of offal? Ox-heart? Her stock of diamonds was diminishing rapidly and to no avail: once again he pushed away his plate untouched.

'You need air. You need exercise. You need company. You do not lead a proper life.'

The Countess clucked. Kind-heartedness ruled her nature but sometimes one was obliged to speak out. Gruber was beginning to look like a skeleton from one of those terrible camps we should all do our best to forget. She stood over him, her pretty hands folded across her pinny.

'Most of us here have been through difficult times but it does not do to dwell on them. Life goes on. Perhaps it would help to talk to me? Or is there something else you fancy?'

The rattle in his throat began, always the first indication that Gruber was about to make one of his rare utterances. The struggle was appalling to watch and Olga, for all her good intentions, dreaded what he might be about to confess. And his voice was now so faint she had to bend uncomfortably close to catch it.

'I remember now.'

'Yes?'

'I am a vegetarian.'

When Gruber had stumped and shuffled his way up to his attic, Olga sat, puffed and utterly bewildered. Almost down to her last diamond. And for nothing! Of course, if it was vegetables he wanted, then vegetables he must have though she herself had never trusted a man who didn't eat meat.

As usual with Olga, resolution won. She put on the spectacles she had found at the jumble sale for Fallen Girls and made a list of menus. No rabbit-food – a man needed at least one cooked meal a day. Turnip stew? Leek soup? Soufflé of swede? Was beetroot in season? She wondered if the greengrocer took diamonds.

After the visit to the police station to report Dido, Elenora, shedding hairpins as she went, could not precisely remember where she was supposed to be. She overcame the impulse, like a hot flush, to enter the Cathedral and slam the door behind her. Several times she thought she had glimpsed the flick of a grey cloak and at least twice she had

imagined she saw a squarish figure in navy blue loitering –
clearly a rapist.

At some point she found herself in her own college (one
of Giles Gilbert Scott's less memorable memorials) deliver-
ing a seminar to a mixed assembly of both sexes, all of
whom would have chosen to be out in the afternoon sun
doing things to each other in the long grass or in punts.
Except, of course, for the nuns who would dedicate their
firsts to the good Lord and go out to teach Chaucer to
bewildered Africans who in their turn would seize on the
more interesting aspects of Christianity. In Nigeria the
Crucifixion was top favourite.

Elenora explained how *The Legend of Good Women* could
be taken as an apologia for *Troilus and Criseyde*. Or was it
the other way round? That was a frightfully good-looking
young man in the third row. Oh, to tousle those smooth
golden locks, to slip a hand inside the open-necked shirt.
And the boy beside him! Low of brow and swarth of hue –
a veritable Caliban. To surrender to him would be to
give way to Nature herself. The scent of the philadelphus
outside the open window was overwhelming. Elenora
undid her top button. She panted.

'"O blisful nyght, of hem so longe isought." '

'Are you all right, Miss Flitch?'

In the front row Sister Michael was watching her with
beady pebble gaze.

'Perfectly, thank you.' Nothing a good fuck wouldn't
cure. 'That is, it is rather hot, I think. If you will excuse
me.'

While Olga worried about sauerkraut, Valerie Mowle
licked her pencil and composed the fifth draft of her letter to
Evelyn Home (Please answer by return of post and do not
print my name, yours faithfully, Anon), Vera went through
Ilse Lamprey's drawers while Ilse lay in the garden hating
birds and flowers, and Rainbird, with shaking hand,
planned his assault upon Radpole Road. While Babakov

84

dozed next to Ilse, catching the sun quite badly and dreaming that he was seven and everything was all right. While Posy lay back in the punt under the willows reading to Janusz: '"It's a little Anxious," he said to himself, "to be a Very Small Animal Entirely Surrounded by Water"', Elenora alighted from the bus, stood as though in perplexity in a deep pool of shade, and plunged down the path to the convent of the Little Flowers of St Anne.

'Come outside, my dear. It's so long since we've seen you. Quite a stranger.'

Regretfully Mother Martin turned off the television. She would never have dreamed cricket could be so interesting. How splendid if England were to win the Ashes in Coronation Year. Not that she had ever quite understood whose ashes they were. A metaphor perhaps. But if so, of what? Netball had been her game.

She watched the picture fade to a dot until that too finally vanished. Extraordinary. She shook her head and at last noticed that Elenora was not herself. Her hair was wild and her top button undone. It was swings and roundabouts, Mother Martin always said. She knew exactly what she had given up thirty years ago. But the habit of obedience, though it had its drawbacks, was a wonderful thing. A less shrewd woman would have said home is where your heart is, here with Christ. Mother Martin knew better. There were all kinds of lives she could have lived and they used to trouble her. No longer now. There was no certainty of ease within or without these walls.

Mother Martin sent a novice for mint tea for one.

'Come. Sit down. Here by the dovecote. The fig has done well this year, don't you think?' She talked on. Elenora would speak in her own good time. She sipped the tea. Her frantic colour faded.

'Mother, you believe in the soul?'

'Naturally.'

Elenora looked up. On the gable one wood pigeon was

85

pursuing another with clear intent. She took a deep breath and looked down at her lap.

'And the body? If you'll forgive me.'

Mother Martin smiled. Privately she had always judged Elenora Flitch to be a shade prim. Much as she enjoyed her company she used to feel she should watch her tongue.

'Well, there's no avoiding it, is there? I mean one lives in it, after all.'

A novice skipped by on the way to feed the doves. While she ran a tight ship and there was nothing, she believed, for which the Church could reproach her, Mother Martin had always found it difficult to stamp on joy.

There was a flutter of wings as the wood pigeons reached consummation. Elenora's voice was very faint.

'I thought perhaps, in your position—'

'Dear Miss Flitch—'

'Please call me Elenora.'

'My name is Ursula. Elenora, there is a popular misconception that those who enter Holy Orders stop going to the lavatory. That somehow we shed our bodies and fail to notice anyone else's. Of course I believe in the body: its pleasures as well as its troubles. Look – there goes Sister Michael. Poor girl, she is so plain, celibacy might have been made for her.'

'But you don't *think* about it.' Elenora blushed. 'I mean – in the way of the world?'

Mother Martin's eyes were pretty and sharp. There was something here but she would have to wait for it to come out.

'Vanity is forbidden, certainly. But no one can proscribe memory. You might not credit it now, but I used to love dancing. Oh, how I loved it! And I nearly married, you know. A gentleman farmer. In Berkshire. Come, let us walk in the orchard.'

It was easier walking but not much.

'You see, I have this feeling that I have lost my soul. That my body is under some evil influence. And I think I know

86

who the influence is.' Elenora stood, rooted in the orchard under the boughs heavy as blessings, her hair falling down, her face ashen. 'Her name is Vera. She is Ilse Lamprey's housekeeper. She is a wraith from hell.'

When she had calmed Elenora with a prayer, a couple of aspirin, a glass of camomile tea laced with a spot of something stronger that had proved helpful for pre-menstrual tension among the novices, handed her a small phial in a silver filigree container and sent her home feeling, she hoped, slightly better, Mother Martin sat at her desk, more troubled than she had revealed to Elenora. Faith and common sense had served her well all her life but at this moment neither seemed quite adequate. Sense said that there was nothing wrong with Elenora a lover couldn't cure. Faith, like an absent-minded angel, was altogether too vague and faery-like to be any use to Elenora who was not, after all, of the Faith.

It was all too fantastic, of course, but then, even though it might be out of fashion nowadays, there was indeed a hell and no reason therefore why it should not send forth daemons to walk the earth, just as saints popped up in the most unlikely places. In this small, quiet place of virgins, Mother Martin discouraged talk of such phenomena as conducive to hysteria, in the same way she disapproved of flagellation or any other form of self-mortification.

And yet forgive me, oh Lord, for unreason – might that terrible war have left open a small door or two giving on to the everlasting fire? Or Purgatory, at least? Through which the souls of the damned might stride. And the tormented and unshriven. That was the worst thought of all: the crowding of spirits who had perished without the benefit of grace and wandered still, calling to each other, carrying their dead babies, some no more than children, all hugging to themselves, like sacks of ashes, their unlived lives.

As the bell announced vespers Mother Martin did her best to collect herself. She was in danger of becoming as fanciful as Elenora Flitch. There was probably a perfectly simple explanation. The poor woman might be suffering some kind of mental breakdown. On the other hand . . . Mother Martin lifted the telephone and dialled Father Clement.

After a sleep induced by the camomile tea and the spot of something else, Elenora was feeling a little better. Whatever she had been so distractedly seeking at the Convent – magic? a miracle? – she had not found, but it had been a release to speak the unspeakable. The sky had not fallen. Vera had not manifested herself wearing her horrid miasma.

By the time she put the key in the lock of her flat, Elenora had almost made up her mind to do as Mother Martin had suggested and have her hair done tomorrow. How lucky women were, she thought. However do men manage without the reassurance of such healing trivia? Hairdressers, clothes, shopping, menus, the biological right to the occasional attack of unreason? Yes, really she should apologise to Mother Martin.

There on the table was a book: the OUP edition of *The Faerie Queene* – presumably from Gustavus. Since Vera had taken over the household keys from Babakov, Vera must have brought in the book. An unpleasant thought but one she could face more comfortably since her visit to Mother Martin. Absently Elenora touched the tiny amulet – or, more precisely, the reliquary – that Mother Martin had lent her. It was absurd, of course, that she should have felt better from the moment she hung round her neck the tiny phial (if anyone asked she could say it was simply a pendant – the water was colourless). Fantastical, in fact, that a normally rational woman of supposedly crisp intellect should, in the middle of the twentieth century, in the very home of reason and wisdom, imagine that she carried between her breasts a single one of the true *lacrimae Christi*. And be glad of it.

And then, as Elenora stood before her mirror in a shaft

88

of early evening sun, poured herself a half-glass of sherry (could Mother Martin have laced that interesting tea?) and sat down in her dove-blue chair, her feet crossed at the ankles, considering such matters and rather wishing she had learned to smoke, it came to her that ancient knowledge so diligently housed and preserved must contain within it all manner of unreason, passion, superstition, extravagance, extravagant faith. Here bones of saints had crackled, death had danced, visions of hell still grinned from the stones, words on precious paper in cloistered libraries were human voices in grief and joy and pain.

So here, after all, was no sanctuary and she had been foolish to expect it. Her rectory childhood had been quiet as a folded blue sheet, her existence since an attempt to continue that out-of-the-world peace. Her parents neatly buried, Elenora had pinned her soul to the small emblems represented in this room: silent books, muted colours, the untroubled ticking of counted hours.

Could what was happening to her now be life in a rage reaching out?

The room seemed suddenly airless, yet at the window the curtains stirred. A hot wind from hell?

A cool bath. Not actually cold but tepid, quite the most refreshing.

Let fancy sulk and useless revelation.

The Lord abide with me and keep my spirit.

Elenora undressed like a nun, eyes closed not to see the peephole bra.

If one could shed as easily the flesh. To be pure spirit.

Close the curtains. There is no one there in the garden wearing a navy-blue belted raincoat.

And I shall live in His house forever.

Go on, get your hair permed. Try a Toni.

Is that Vera in the passage? Lock the door. Can the damned slip through a keyhole?

So tired.

I pray the Lord my soul to take.

At last, there was Elenora in bed, her long grey hair plaited, between cool sheets, poor widowed Aeneas at her feet, the bright day and the summer evening gone. She touched again the tear of our Lord or it might be Jordan water or even straight from the tap, and only then opened Gustavus's Spenser and read:

> A lesson too too hard for living clay
> From love in course of nature to refraine.

She was already in that dim land halfway to sleep when from her own eye there slipped the first tear she had ever shed.

Babakov called in Shadow from the garden. The rhododendron bush looked larger than usual but even wearing his spectacles Babakov had no night sight to speak of. He sighed, turned back indoors, wearier than he could ever remember being. He had become as possessed as Ilse Lamprey used to be by the notion of Elenora pursued by suitors, though in his fantasy she remained pure as Penelope. His legs would not take him as far as the bus-stop. Odysseus unmanned, all he could do was to watch and to worry.

Shadow raced in from the darkness as if the hounds of hell were after her, past Babakov and down the basement stairs. Babakov grunted and closed the door. Vera's job to lock now. No use to anyone any more, old Babakov. And what business was it of his anyway, if Elenora Flitch took to herself every man in England? He shook his heavy head and turned his attention to Shadow who had leaped from the chair to the top of the wardrobe and was glaring down, lashing her tail, her mouth open in the soundless curse.

Gruber too was close to tears. His hands shook as, with the attic door locked and Vera standing over him, he dipped into the chamois leather bag for a nugget of gold the size of a small fingernail.

'More,' said Vera, and he dipped again.

'How you can do this. And to me of all men.'

'Easily. To you in particular. *Mein lieber Vater.*'

Vera was enjoying herself. She really looked quite pretty. Yes, it had all definitely been worth the trouble.

'How you can say that!' He clutched the leather bag to his bowed-in chest. 'You are a terrible dream. You do not exist.'

'The Stempfle letter says I do.'

'Stempfle is dead. I ordered.'

'As you ordered her death?'

'Never!'

'How can you know, from so many? And remember: I am my father's daughter.'

Now the tears did come, with pain, between his fingers, as though a stone cracked and wept.

'I loved her. How could I kill her? She was the first and the last. The other was nothing. A shop girl.'

'Yet my mother was killed. Don't tell me you believe that suicide nonsense.'

Rage now. 'I was betrayed. Again! *Der treue Heinrich.* As at the last. Even then.'

Gruber stood, clenched his fists and began his pacing, shoulders hunched to avoid the sloping ceiling of the attic (one floor below, Olga Rákosfalvi nodded: early tonight). His left arm hung a little slack as did the flesh on his frame and the deepset eyes that burned so fearfully were dead as coals put out. Vera made herself comfortable on the bed.

'You're not frightening me, you know.'

Gruber wiped his hand across his eyes. He clutched the area of his heart.

'You are a ghost! You come from hell. You will be the death of me.'

'No need for that. Just hand over the gold and I'll go away.'

'Blackmail! My own flesh and blood!'

'Ah! So you do acknowledge me.'

'I acknowledge nothing.'

'Not that it matters. Knowing what I know.'

Defeated, Gruber sank into the only chair.

'Go. Go!'

'Very well. For the moment.'

Humming to herself, Vera tripped downstairs. A light under Ilse Lamprey's door. She seemed to be talking to someone, or perhaps it was the telephone. Vera considered eavesdropping but she had had enough fun for one night. Besides, there was a nice bone to finish in her room. Half an hour later she – and all the household – was disturbed by shouts from the garden.

'To whom am I speaking?'

Although she had a telephone in her room Ilse Lamprey never used it since there was no one among the living she could imagine wishing to address. She held the receiver therefore cautiously some distance from her mouth and ear and spoke as though projecting her voice from Radpole Road to the police station two miles across town.

'Police Constable Bright, madam. Can I help you?'

Alone in the station, Bright put down reluctantly the new statistical bulletin on prostitute murders in the Home Counties (sub-heading Necrophilia) and straightened his tie.

Faintly Ilse boomed: 'I wish to report a burglar. Or it may be a rapist. In my garden.'

Lately, Ilse had almost given up going to bed. Perhaps she was dreaming upright in her wheelchair by the window but it appeared that the phantasms around her house were gathering, thickening: at least taking on more solid flesh. She had not yet decided whether to be glad or sorry when a passing car had lit up what was beyond doubt an opaque and sturdy figure crouched among the rhododendrons. In a way she had become attached to her ghosts. She knew where she was with them and as long as they were fantasies could make of them what she chose: marauding nuns, Elenora Flitch's lovers, burglars, revenants from her own past: her mother and father as she used to watch them from her nursery window, forgetful as ever of her, arms entwined, her father whispering in her mother's ear, her mother's head dipping, as they strolled under a full moon in that other dark garden. Considering how few people there were for whom she had cared a jot, there was an astonishing number of shades. Once a garden party. Once the circus at Wien to which Ilse's Berlin banker father had taken her: clowns, fire-eaters, white ponies and dancing bears.

Ilse had watched it all, horrified, entranced. Her imaginings had grown remarkable as she lost her grip upon the rage that had sustained her for so long. Though she still had a tongue sharp as a whip.

'To whom am I speaking? You sound like a child. How old are you?'

PC Bright flinched and stroked the downy moustache he was trying to grow. He sat to attention.

'Madam. If you were to give me your name and address.'

'My name has nothing to do with it. The address is 161 Radpole Road.'

'And your grounds for suspicion?'

'I am not suspicious. I am certain that there is a person in my shrubbery. You are to come at once.' Ilse put down the telephone.

Bright looked at the clock. Detective Sergeant Rainbird was due back. He told the telephonist to take messages, combed his hair (centre parting) in the gents, studied his pubescent moustache for signs of thickening, left the station and climbed on his bike. The woman sounded foreign and it was probably her own husband having a pee in the flowerbed. All the same. A stitch in nine. A bird in the bush. Initiative. Willingness to take responsibility. After the blunder with the Detective Sergeant the other day a spot of nifty apprehension and maybe even a little felony charge would show up nicely on his next review.

'Oh yes, Ilse Lamprey, there is certainly something.' Babakov, peering as instructed, could make out nothing at all but he had long ago learned to agree with everything Ilse said, while thinking at the same time of something more interesting. All the same, for once, he felt he had to demur.

'Was it altogether wise, I wonder, to bring in the police? If they were to enter the house.'

Ilse was agitated. The moment she put down the receiver she had realised her mistake.

'They must not enter! Babakov – you must stop them. Telephone them now and tell them not to come. This minute! Tell them it was a mistake. Tell them anything.'

Babakov dialled.

Vera by the pantry slept the sleep of the truly evil.

The Countess dreamed of a wide meadow, a blue sky and children at play.

Elenora tossed, mumbling in her shallow sleep.

Janusz and Posy were wide awake, sharing the bed with Posy's virginity. Posy had said, since you got gated if you came in after half past ten it was better to stay out all night and hope the nuns at the hostel wouldn't check.

In the rhododendrons Rainbird was panting for a pee and wondering if a night approach had been such a good idea when he was struck violently from behind and flung to the ground by an assailant who had the advantage of surprise, youth and ambition. Yelling, the two tumbled on the lawn as lights came on inside the house.

'No one is to open the door!' called Ilse from the top of the stairs. 'It is the rapist of Radpole Road.'

Elenora yawned, nodded and went back to bed.

Rainbird bellowed, elbowed his attacker in the groin and ran.

Chapter Nine

'"Speak in French when you can't think of the English for a thing – turn out your toes as you walk,"' Posy read. 'Oh, Janusz, sit down. *Alice* doesn't mean what it says. I can't think why Ilse Lamprey told you to read it. Anyway you can't speak French either.'

Janusz shook his head, then brightened.

'I am washing.'

'Washing up. Yes, I know you are. And it's very good you got that job at the Blenheim Arms.'

Posy sighed. Lovely though it was to be with Janusz, he did complicate her life. Apart from the fact that she had hardly any room in her head for thoughts of anything but him, she had lost almost all her friends because she felt Janusz would be too difficult to explain and so she did not try. She parried both questions and suitors and no longer ranged her many invitations on the mantelshelf in her hostel bed-sitter. Since she became increasingly certain that she and Janusz would make love properly before very long, she supposed she ought to be finding out about contraception but so far as she could gather, in this Elizabethan age, professional advice was available only to those who could prove or pretend that they were getting married. She knew about French letters but could hardly imagine herself sending Janusz to the barber's to ask for Durex. There were girls who did it, she was aware, but was too shy to find out what they did about babies. Or rather, not babies.

Elenora Flitch was her moral tutor but how could you explain to anyone so perfect and unworldly that you wished immorally to dispose of your virginity? Besides, Miss Flitch had not looked herself lately. Her hair fell down and she was confused in tutorials.

At least Janusz had a job. For washing-up they did not ask for work permits.

'Come on, darling, you have to learn.'

Janusz beamed. How proud he looked. How Posy loved him!

'I learn time.'

'Good. That's wonderful. Tell me then – no, Janusz, please stop kissing me there – what time is it?' Posy pointed to the cheap alarm clock Janusz had bought with his first week's money after he had spent the rest on a single white rose for Posy (she had pressed it between the pages of *Metaphysical Poets: Donne to Butler*).

'Brillig!' said Janusz.

'What? Oh dear. Of course. *Jabberwocky*.' It was four o'clock in the morning. Brillig was afternoon. 'But, please, Janusz, no more *Alice*.'

The book slid to the floor. Janusz slid on top of Posy.

'Boosom,' he said. 'Tommy. Tommy hole.'

As he grazed on her navel Posy did not bother to correct him. She felt like a meadow, a whole field, a country, the planet, the universe, laid out in welcome and sheer delight.

This same night of the business of the rapist of Radpole Road, Gustavus had been sleeping in college (trying to dream of Ilse Lamprey whose sneer had for some reason grown fainter lately, as though there were interference in the ether) and so had missed everything. In particular, the presence this time not of one but two policemen in Valerie Mowle's kitchen.

Not that the younger had lingered. The older and squarer one in the navy-blue raincoat Valerie herself had mended not so long ago spoke in a way Valerie could only describe as unpleasant though she caught but a few words, most of which seemed to concern the parts of a policeman (or indeed of any man) she preferred not to consider. Something to do with putting things through the mangle and turning them into tripe.

As she hung her gardening hat on the door and pulled a cardie over her flannel nightie Valerie heard an odd sound behind her. Rather like the noise the sink made when it became unblocked.

'Oh dear,' she said. 'I'm sure there's nothing to cry about.'

The glimpse of Valerie's flannelled bosoms under the *Woman's Weekly* fantasy rib cardigan and the events of the night served only to unman Rainbird further. He choked and mopped his face with the large, no longer very white handkerchief he had given himself last Christmas (wrapped it up in seasonal paper and all, with card and greetings).

'Dear madam, you must forgive me. A difficult day.'

'Of course.' Valerie was surprised to find she was getting quite used to Rainbird. Even when he wasn't there she had a feeling that he was – rather like her friend. It had passed through her mind that he might be a rapist but rapists surely did not sit in your own kitchen crying over spotted dick?

'If there is anything I can do? To help?'

'If you could remove your dear doggie from my ankle bone.'

'Cuffy! Let go at once! I'm so sorry.'

'That's all right, madam. I've always had a fancy for dogs.' Dead.

It was marvellous what thick tea with six lumps could do to restore a man to himself. Company included. Very much included. Warm buttocks in soft feather bed. WX rayon knickers steaming on the clothes horse before the Aga.

Rainbird sighed with exhausted contentment laced with lust. Valerie looked up from her knitting – a curious garment that had started as a matinée jacket for the issue of her phantom pregnancy but had at some point beyond her control developed four legs (or arms, however you cared to see it). Maybe it would do for Cuffy in cold weather? His coat was getting very thin. No, too small. Just about right for a corgi. A zip under the tummy perhaps? But what about the tail?

'You poor man. You really are tired. I think you work too hard. All men do. I do hope Mrs Rainbird takes proper care of you. Suet pudding and flannel next to the skin!'

Rainbird wagged his head. What a change it was, thought Valerie, to have a man who sat down at the table and ate his pudding. Now she looked at him properly there was something about the way his eyebrows met in the middle.

'Alas, I am an orphan.'

'But how terrible!'

She's melting. Steady, boy, steady. Under the table Rainbird slapped the hand that would have reached out for a grope beneath the fantasy rib. His eyes grew smaller still with passion but for all he knew hubby was sleeping upstairs. Besides, it had been a long day and there was the pleasing prospect of young Bright waiting at the station in terror. He stood.

'Duty calls. You'll let me know then? If anything transpires?'

'Transpires?' Valerie felt quite weak, wobbly, foolish like the girl she had somehow never been.

'Across the road.'

'Oh yes. Of course. The Fifth Column. I remember now.'

'The plot thickens.'

'Oh dear, does it?'

'If walls could speak.'

'I often think it's just as well they can't.' Faintly.

'A nest of vipers.'

'Oh, I do agree!'

Almost, Valerie Mowle told Rainbird about Elenora

Flitch stealing Gustavus. Almost he confided the true purpose of his long and dedicated mission.

Once Valerie Mowle had despatched the Detective Sergeant she sat down again still rather a'flutter and opened today's *Woman's Home* (after their failure to answer her letter Anon and most urgent by return of post, she had cancelled *Woman*).

While Cuffy snored and twitched in a dog-dream of cats, rabbits, policemen's ankles and a nice roll in the compost heap, Valerie read into the small hours of the night. How to make your marriage a honeymoon every day: one hundred ways with mince. Queen for a Day – now this was more interesting. Write in your own words (well, whose words would you write in, thought Valerie) one day from the Queen's private diary and win a fortnight for two. It didn't actually say where the fortnight would be and Valerie could not quite imagine Gustavus on a fortnight for two. Nevertheless, perhaps she would have a try. Few could be better placed than she. Or would it be a betrayal of trust, bearing in mind the intimacy of her relationship with her friend? She turned the pages and came upon her stars for the week: time for romance as a dark stranger with eyebrows that meet in the middle enters your life! A message! Clearly intended for her alone! From someone called Gypsy Allengro.

Really, this had turned into the most astonishing day. Or rather, night, Valerie mused, at last in bed where sleep evaded her and with Cuffy comfy on Gustavus's pillow she thought of that second when Rainbird on leaving seemed about to confide something. To blot out the disturbing image of the Detective Sergeant, as the birds on every bough began to sing Valerie rehearsed: Dear Diary, as a dog-lover and mother of two . . .

At about the time Valerie Mowle finally fell asleep, Rainbird was on the milk train to London with a view to interviewing a certain alien antiquarian bookseller arrested in Victoria for

99

the sale of pornographic literature whose address corresponded with the scrap of paper rootled out of the dustbin of 161 Radpole Road. A second meeting but this time in the favourable climate of the interrogation room where inspired guesses might be triumphantly confirmed. Rainbird took out his notepad and pencil; his list read:

> Gottlieb
> Entry to Radpole Rd.
> Search warrant?
> Cat Dido
> E. Flitch
> Subject: grey cloak, female Person
> Insp. Fox Paddington Green?
> Bright

At the passing of the train England looked up – until you reached the outskirts of London, still a land the first Elizabethans might have recognised. Viridian green rain-soaked meadows. Sweet slow rivers. Soft-haired willows. Pond with ducks. Villages sleeping unaware of proposed invasion of industrial estates, dormitory suburbs. Black and white cows returning from hand-milking to lush pasture.

Of all this Rainbird was oblivious, as he struck out both search warrant and Insp. Fox. Solo mission this. No credit shared. Final target glory and Mrs Mowle.

Bright, on the other hand, he underlined and circled. A terrible smile creased the Detective Sergeant's face as his head nodded and he slept at last, content.

A low was forming in the Atlantic with plans for England but around the Convent the morning air was tremulously beautiful, bright as a girl before she falls. Mother Martin, unusually restless, had been wondering since six o'clock how early she dare ring Father Clement. She knew better than to disturb him at breakfast but by eight o'clock could no longer contain herself. He had been unavailable yesterday afternoon and meanwhile her agitation had grown beyond what she would normally acknowledge as reasonable.

'Well, of course, not the true *lacrimae Christi*! How could it be. But the poor woman seemed nearly deranged.'

Father Clement nodded. He had always found Mother Martin the most sensible of women – a pleasure to do business with. He permitted himself from time to time a harmless fantasy that had he not started life as the fifth son of a bookie's runner without prospects and had he not been called, the two of them might have made a most satisfactory marriage. Sitting in the orchard while the novices fluttered round with tea and home-made scones, he would half-close his eyes and imagine this was his garden and she his wife. A woman of virtue, prettiness and humour, he saw her walking up a garden path with a trug full of flowers. This morning, however, she was almost babbling.

'I don't believe there is any cause for repentance. There is great power in the placebo. Tell me, of what faith is this young lady?'

'She has baths here sometimes. I suppose she's the same as us – C of E.'

'She has not the faith then?'

'I doubt it. At least in a formal way. Though the reliquary – I mean the water – did seem to calm her. And she is very concerned about hell.'

'Well now, that is unusual. Quite out of fashion. Can you be more specific?'

Mother Martin explained. Father Clement scratched his chin.

'Pity she's not a Papist. They get this kind of thing every day. I don't suppose she'd care to convert? I could call Farm Street? No? Well, in that case I think we can only bide our time. Wait and pray. Even if there were an emissary in Radpole Road one can hardly exorcise someone else's housekeeper without a by-your-leave. If one were licensed to exorcise.'

'Thank you, Father.'

'Please. Call upon me at any time. Meanwhile it could be that her best resort would be the medical profession. I have observed before an hysteria peculiar to the unattached female academic of a certain age, particularly in the more ancient universities. Perhaps a Christian marriage?'

'I'm sure you're right.'

Of course Father Clement was right. He must be. All the same, Mother Martin felt faintly let down as she rang off. She loved Elenora. She feared for her, dreaded even the faintest possibility that across the road there really was something hellish going on.

She walked out into the air as the clear bell rang. It was clouding over from the west.

After the drama of the night it had taken 161 Radpole Road some time to come to its wits (except for Janusz and Posy who had already quite lost their wits and spent every waking hour in joyous bed, breaking off only for Janusz to pedal groggily on Posy's bicycle to his washing-up job at the Blenheim Arms).

Once over her folly at sending for the police and her relief that they had not entered the house, Ilse Lamprey, sitting up wigless in her wheelchair, found herself confused in her attitude to rapists. She consulted her list for the first time for days. There was an inconsistency in disliking both virgins and lovers since how could a virgin cease to be a virgin without the attentions of a lover? Now she came to think about it the only answer was rape. All rather disturbing. She would put her mind to it tomorrow if she remembered. Meanwhile she had an addition to make to her list: policemen.

By the afternoon Elenora Flitch was receiving Derrick Sproke – the Caliban of the seminar – for his Chaucer tutorial.

102

Whatever had happened in the night (it was becoming increasingly difficult to distinguish dream from reality) had left her languid in a way that was not altogether unpleasant. After lemon tea and a Huntley and Palmers breakfast biscuit, she had consulted her diary, thought about having her hair done, but instead observed that it was a sunny morning and wandered into the garden where the Countess was weeding.

Olga Rákosfalvi looked up, puffed.

'A rapist, my dear! In Radpole Road! Who would believe it?'

'Oh yes, I'd believe it. I think I remember now.'

Elenora wore a rather girlish frock, not her usual style, lawn with little tucks and flounces. She was barefoot in the dew. She smiled vaguely, at the Countess or the morning.

'Do you know, I couldn't get Dr Gruber out of his room for breakfast. He doesn't even answer. Gardens are very soothing, don't you think?'

'Very.' That queer smile again. And Elenora's hair was hanging down almost to her waist, like a veil.

'Are you all right, Miss Flitch? You don't look quite yourself.'

'I suppose that depends upon who one is. Oneself.'

Olga stood. Sometimes it was hard to hold on to common sense.

'I do recommend nettles. Boiled, of course. Iron. Ferrous sulphate in any form is very restoring. Oh, what a pretty pendant! Is it silver?'

'A tear,' said Elenora. 'Just a tear.'

Olga shook her head and got on with her gardening. The redeeming thing about life, she supposed, was that one had never seen everything, there was always the possibility of surprise. Only half an hour later did she realise that she had been pulling up not weeds, but flowers.

By mid-afternoon the rain was falling heavily as Elenora heard from a great distance her own voice explaining to low-browed Derrick Sproke the influence of anti-feminist literature upon Chaucer in general and the portrait of the Wife of Bath in particular.

'Once again we return to the French *Roman* and the portrait of La Vieille, among many other satires against women. Boccaccio is another possible source. Ah yes, you have noted him in your essay.' Elenora held up the fruit of Sproke's night labour by the corner between finger and thumb. A poor little thing it was, grubby and coffee-stained, written on blue lined paper in a rounded script that fell sometimes on its back then on its face. All the same, she knew she would give him a beta plus for the whorls of black hair that curled from beneath frayed and greasy cuffs.

Where was she? Ah yes.

'You will have observed the broadness – one might say the bawdiness of her speech: she is inviting the grosser attentions. Let us see, in her Prologue. Yes there we are, line 32 and then 75 – perhaps you would read?' While I study that interesting bulge in your corduroy crotch.

The boy read, one hirsute finger with dirty nail tracing each word.

'Quite. References to bigamy and octogamy, general scorn for virginity. And all supported by holy Scripture.' It was almost dark now, the false twilight of a rainy day. Elenora had difficulty catching her breath. She stood, paced her small room. 'You have a button loose,' she said, 'in your fly,' while she, standing above him, unbuttoned herself. Ah, the bulge swelled and increased! Caliban's mouth fell open.

'What she is saying, I think,' Elenora concluded, 'is that God wanted us to have sex or he wouldn't have invented it.' Her dress lay in a pretty puddle at her feet. Curled on the back of her dove-blue chair, Aeneas flicked the tip of his tail. 'Don't you agree?'

'Ug. Yes.'

Bewildered, flattered, excited and afraid, the low-browed Sproke gazed up at his tutor's pale candle-flamed shape, white as wax, wavering it seemed to him in the gathering shades. And with one finger beckoning. He wondered if he ought to keep his gown on and wished he'd washed his socks.

'Come!'

'Miss Flitch—'

'Courage! I wol use my instrument as frely as my Makere hath it sent!'

Spread upon her virgin sheet, Elenora opened wide her arms and closed her eyes.

As the rain fell down and an illusion of premature night came upon Radpole Road, Vera was in her element: her ear to Elenora's door, her eye to Ilse Lamprey's keyhole while her expectations frolicked happily in Gruber's attic. The thickening of plots was her daily bread – all that puzzled her was that anyone could be so gullible. Any doubts about her own substance had long disappeared. It was the people around her who seemed the hopeless, fettered spirits living in a hell of their own making. She was simply cleverer than the rest. She had known from the first that she was born into hell.

Gustavus arrived home soaked to the skin. Turning into Radpole Road, he considered calling on Elenora Flitch for a nice chat about Spenser. Such a peaceful woman and, now he had come to see her in the role of Gloriana, rather attractive. Not exactly pretty – nearer beautiful. But the light in her ground-floor flat was out and in any case she was so far above him, beyond reproach, so quietly queenly, she had probably never noticed him and if she had would regard him as no more interesting than the ground upon which she trod in those soft suede pumps of palest grey.

Besides, he thought, I am mad. I have lost my soul and only Ilse Lamprey can give it back.

There was nothing for supper and he had forgotten the shopping list. His only hope was not to disturb Valerie, which meant climbing in through the downstairs lavatory window and going to sleep in his study. Shoes off, he slid inside his own house and tiptoed down the passage. Out of the dark leaped the hound from hell: Cuffy yapping Coff Coff, fastened to Gustavus's shin.

'Rape!' called Valerie from upstairs. 'The rapist of Radpole Road!'

The Atlantic low moved east and by the evening was settled comfortably over London, where Detective Sergeant Rainbird interviewed the antiquarian bookseller, Gottlieb, in a windowless interrogation room.

'Naughty stories, eh?' he said. 'And illustrated, I daresay. But that's not what we have to talk about, is it?'

Gottlieb sighed. He had thought himself beyond astonishment but he found it hard to believe in Rainbird – a species of Englishman he had imagined to be confined to the cinema screen and the theatre. Yet he had felt faintly uneasy ever since this clown had appeared in Victoria, clutching a grubby piece of paper bearing his own address, purloined apparently from Ilse Lamprey's dustbin.

The Detective Sergeant circled the table once, paused, rocked on his heels, then wheeled and thrust his face into the victim's. Gottlieb shuddered not with terror but distaste.

'A little matter of undesirable foreign nationals,' he breathed hotly. 'Illegal immigration in which you, I have cause to believe, have played a major part.'

Gottlieb tried not to breathe in.

'Nothing has been proved and even if it had, I fail to see how I can help you.'

Rainbird's whisper was more awful than his voice.

'Names! Between you and me. And one name in particular. You know who.'

106

'I have no idea what you are talking about.'

Rainbird drew back, paced again, then whirling on his heel, turned the lamp directly on Gottlieb's face. The old man blinked. Rainbird in this stance reminded him of someone. When he remembered who it was he had to suppress a smile.

'When was it? '45? '46? I have it on record that the woman Lamprey purchased the house in Radpole Road in the late winter of 1946.'

'Indeed?' Gottlieb did his best to pretend he was somewhere else (with his dear boys when Wien was still fun, in the apartment full of mirrors and young tender men, so sweet, so wild) but the smell of wet mackintosh was too much. He was too old for this sort of thing. He wanted to go home if he could remember where home was.

'I have not been charged. I demand my release. I have nothing more to say.'

He closed his eyes. When he opened them this ridiculous policeman would have disappeared. Ah, he did seem to be on the way out. First though, in a voice reminiscent of Boris Karloff, he made certain promises regarding his return and some very peculiar plans he had for the prisoner involving a number of mechanical aids, including a sausage machine and curling tongs.

In the early hours of the morning Rainbird was back at his desk in the station, his already dodgy temper not improved by a telephone call from somewhere in Whitehall to the effect that he was to lay off the antiquarian bookseller of Austrian extraction who was to be charged under the dirty books law and released on nominal bail.

He ignored a message from Fox of Paddington Green. A hush-up if ever he saw one. So close and yet so far! With shaking hand he consulted his crumpled list. Cat Dido at least remained and E. Flitch. Then as the dawn broke wetly, Rainbird remembered there was something quite satisfactory to be going on with.

'Bright,' he called gently and contemplated the fact that a silver lining for one is for someone else a cloud.

'Perhaps we're doing it the wrong way? Just one more try?'

Derrick Sproke groaned and prayed for the dawn which, were it not for another downpour, would surely have come.

He, on the other hand, had not merely not come but failed even to penetrate his tutor. That is to say, enthusiastic after his initial shock, he had entered but come up against an unexpected impediment. Although he had never met one before (his experience being limited to frustrating gropes and clutches) he took this to be a hymen which seemed, in view of Elenora's flagrant invitation, surprising. (Perhaps they grew over again? He wished devoutly that he knew more about female physiology but as a freshman he had hardly progressed below breasts.)

Oh, what a night it had been as the rain fell down outside and poor Derrick moiled and toiled upon an eager but impenetrable Elenora. How she panted, how he groaned, till by midnight, half-fainting he rolled off her and on to his back in a sweat.

'I'm sorry, Miss Flitch. I'm afraid you've made a mistake. I haven't done this before.'

'You are a virgin? Oh dear, so am I. Perhaps we should have a cup of tea before we carry on.'

By the time she returned with the tea, Sproke was snoring. In the moonlight Mother Martin's reliquary winked. Elenora pushed it quickly into a drawer, drank her tea, took a deep breath and climbed back into bed. Chaucer was all very well but hardly explicit enough for this situation. She could not blame the wretched Sproke for being a virgin, though she had in her innocence assumed that any man knew how to without instruction. Was there something she should be doing, she wondered? Perhaps gasping with desire was not enough?

Ah! Sproke still snored but his instrument did not. Hopefully, she stroked it and it uncurled further. Then went back to sleep.

'Mr Sproke,' whispered Elenora, desperately, 'please wake up!'

When at last Elenora slept, Derrick crept like a burglar from her bed, half pulled on his clothes and slipped out of the house. Four eyes saw him go. Aeneas's – amber and unblinking – and Ilse Lamprey's. Another rapist, she supposed, or a burglar, or a lover, or a figment. It was hardly worth the effort. All the same she rapped on the window with her cane and Derrick, still half-buttoned, ran.

Ilse reached for her grey wig. I shall be old, she thought, I shall turn to ash. And then who will dream of me?

Chapter Ten

So many dreams. Dream upon dream. Albion dozed in sands of Empire lost. England dreamed of waking to old times gone, a good summer and a new Queen.

Ilse Lamprey dreamed of Hoovering up everything – secret cats, nuns, virgins, lovers, rapists, policemen, figments, flowers, memory, Elenora Flitch, Vera, Gruber; the final solution, the ultimate spring-clean. She woke to hear Vera crashing and thumping with the vacuum-cleaner. Vera had been in a bad temper lately. Not that one saw much of her but there were intimations of her mood. The little snacks she made for Ilse were no longer so tasty (some smelled quite foul) and there were days she forgot them altogether, so unless Babakov happened to wake from his own dream-life, Ilse was obliged to survive for hours on end from her biscuit-tin. Instead of cleaning Elenora's room Vera put dust in it. Aeneas sneezed and ran under the bed.

What Vera wanted was Gruber's gold and ever since the night of the rapist of Radpole Road he had locked himself in his attic.

The Countess was in despair. As she said to Elenora who wasn't listening: 'Such delicious parsnip faggots and a nice Woolton pie! I leave them outside the door but he hardly pecks at them. Have you found your pussy yet, dear?'

Elenora smiled her new wobbly smile that looked as though she had stuck it on in a hurry and any moment it might slip. She shook her head. Olga Rákosfalvi watched her go. So well turned out, she used to be. Nowadays Elenora appeared to be half-unbuttoned most of the time

110

and this morning she was wearing her grey hair down and odd shoes: one blue, one red. The Countess sighed and went back to the handy book she had found in the library sale: *Cooking from your Allotment, One Hundred Recipes*. Whatever, she wondered, could have turned a once fine man like Dr Gruber into a vegetarian? Love, she supposed: it was dreadful what it did to men. One moment, there they were, striding round, lords of the earth, the next destroyed.

Now, towards the end of May, the University Coronation sub-committee had actually woken up long enough to finalise the arrangements for the great day. The Town was to have its distasteful jollifications. As for the Gown, Gloriana's barge was to proceed from the ferry landing at the end of Radpole Road, embarking nine p.m., arriving St Jude's meadow at ten thirty precisely to floodlights, fire-works and attendant musicke, at just the moment the Town would light its bonfire. The kind of happy compromise at which England was so adept. At some point Elenora's idea of a medieval fair had been handed over to the University Dramatic Society along with the freedom for the evening of Wheatmarket Street. All very satisfactory and perhaps time for a little dry sherry? Miss Flitch? Where is Miss Flitch?

'Have you seen Miss Flitch?'

Babakov had just dropped off to sleep. Not that his dreams were so good any more. Gone were the teasing girls, gone was his mother's sweet smile. He strolled no longer between scented hedgerows or looked out from a warm room upon larch forests and white hills bosomy with snow. Now he stumbled upon clinkers through a burned city under a sky the colour of ash. I am dreaming, he thought and struggled to wake.

'Olga Rákosfalvi! I'm sorry. Please come in.'

'Please, Babakov dear, don't get up. I thought Elenora

111

might be with you but she must be out. However, now I'm here, I hope you will come to a birthday party? Informal, of course.'

Babakov half rose from his chair.

'I would be honoured. Might I ask whose birthday?'

'Ah. That was a slight problem. It wouldn't be yours, I suppose?'

'I'm afraid not.'

'Or Ilse Lamprey's?'

'No.'

'Well then, it will have to be mine. You see, I thought everyone needed cheering up. Who knows, we might even get Dr Gruber down.' The Countess herself seemed more distracted than usual. Her scarves were in disarray and she appeared to be getting her courage together. 'Tell me, Babakov, I have no right to ask, but you and Ilse Lamprey are the only ones who can give me an answer and I am so worried about him. Who is Dr Gruber?'

Babakov let out a long puff of something like despair and lowered himself into the chair with the broken springs. It was raining again.

'I am very sorry. I have the greatest esteem for you, Olga Rákosfalvi, but I cannot give you an answer. It is more than my life is worth.'

'Of course. I understand.'

Olga didn't. But never mind. The thought of the party had quite taken her over. She couldn't remember when she had last had a birthday and wondered how old she would be. Fifty? Forty-nine perhaps, if she wore her best green velvet turban with the feather.

In the course of the next few days the sun came out and went in, the late narcissi in St Jude's meadow opened their white faces of cheerfulness, stood up and were bashed down by a small hailstorm. They struggled up again smiling bravely against all odds – for those who cared to scan nature for signs, emblems of hope.

At the same time a number of interviews were taking place.

Rainbird had an uncomfortable half hour with his Detective Superintendent who appeared less than pleased by his Detective Sergeant's freelance snooping and made it clear that if Rainbird were not to desist from his investigation of a certain house in Radpole Road, someone upstairs would be unhappy. Ours not to reason why.

What fools they were, thought Rainbird. If only they knew. Did they know? If so, they should be exposed and he, Rainbird, would be the one to do it. His bottom would fit very comfortably into the Super's chair.

Meanwhile he retired to his desk and passed a satisfactory half hour preparing a detailed memorandum upon the mental instability of PC Bright and his unsuitability for a career in the force.

He then studied the private file he kept in his locked drawer. This time his assault upon Radpole Road would be all above board. Even the Super could not object to helping some dear old biddy find her missing mog. With a red pencil he circled: E. Flitch.

E. Flitch herself, at the time she was missing from the Coronation committee, was only half an hour late for an interview with the Principal of St Agnes's. It was a wonder, in fact, that she had got there at all. Since the terrible episode with Sproke, Elenora had felt herself to be a ball of knitting wool, unravelling. As though her soul had been caught on a thistle tree and with each tug a little less of her remained. She no longer looked in the mirror for fear of what she would see, nor in her diary which seemed irrelevant to the distracted creature she now was. For all she knew, her face had gone. Certainly the smile she tried to improvise for the Principal felt lopsided.

'Miss Flitch,' said Dame Hilda, who had climbed the

Atlas mountains several times. 'Elenora, I have to tell you frankly there has been a falling off.'

'Off?'

'Please. Let me continue. I had always regarded you as the best kind of academic woman – one to justify our charter before the world. I have here a list of twelve tutorials cancelled, three seminars missed. Could it be that you have something on your mind? Something worrying you?'

Sex. Hell.

'I'm sorry, Principal?'

'If there is anything you wish to tell me?'

'Oh no! Nothing. I haven't been too well lately. A summer cold?'

A burning fever below the belt.

'Indeed. They can be troublesome.'

Elenora reached into her pocket for a handkerchief. What was Dame Hilda talking about?

'So we'll leave it there for the moment. I had always regarded you as the most promising of the younger fellows. I hope I shall not be disappointed.'

'Oh, I do hope not! Thank you so much, Principal.'

All I seem to have left, thought Elenora, as she walked unseeing into the soft rain, is my manners. And my virginity. What was the use of life calling out if she could not answer? Was her problem normal or was Sproke inadequate?

'No, dear Elenora,' said Mother Martin, 'I would not consider it. It would be a delight of course to me to have you among us, but your future lies in the world. I see a husband, several children and a successful part-time academic career.'

'Yes, that will do nicely,' said Valerie Mowle's friend, who had dropped in unexpectedly between fittings to take the weight off her feet. 'What fun. I'm glad you've chosen to write about Balmoral – as in your beautiful home it is somewhere One can really be Oneself. Now, how can I help? Don't forget the mutton puddin's and the dorgis, of course.'

Valerie looked up from the blue-lined paper headed: A Day in the Life of the Queen. Lilibet had absolutely insisted on helping, so it couldn't be cheating.

'Did you say dawgies?'

'No. Dorgis. Quite Our favourite. A cross between a corgi and a dachshund. One dresses casually but One always wears One's pearls. I *do* hope you win. Mr Hartnell will be furious but perhaps just one more fairy cake?'

Olga Rákosfalvi prepared for her party. She slipped her little cards under every door. At the bottom of the bag she had carried through so many countries and so much fearful history, she found an ostrich feather, half a dozen sequins and a bottle of colourless liquid she took to be the last of Max's vodka. Cheerfully she tipped it into the pan with the ingredients she had culled somewhat wildly from the *Young Wives' Wartime Wine Book* she had found at the last meeting of the Mothers' Union. Wrong time of year for hawthorn berries but she had plenty of May blossom, primrose flowers, dandelion and a good slosh of the chemist's tonic Gruber had refused to take. No one would notice if it weren't quite right as that nice young Janusz had brought her a bottle of brandy from the Blenheim Arms. Which all went to show how half the world didn't know how the other half lived. It was just her turn to be the wrong half, that was all. And when she thought of poor Dr Gruber how could she not see herself as blessed?

What plots, what fancies, what confusions and delusions were centred upon 161 Radpole Road where everyone prepared for Olga's party.

Janusz and Posy got out of bed.

Vera's long nose twitched. She sniffed fun to which she had not been invited. It was a fine evening. She put on her grey cloak. A good night for hunting. She wished she were a wraith from hell.

What a small thing is life, thought Ilse. What a fuss about something so quickly done. One angry breath taken and in five minutes we are put out at the back door, as furious as though it mattered what happened in between.

'Don't you think?' she said to Gustavus Mowle, who had as usual cut himself shaving and wore a piece of cotton wool to staunch that absurdly precious life's blood. 'Don't you think it's all rather a disappointment?'

'No, I don't actually. That is, it needn't be.' Ilse was arranged on Olga's bed, Gustavus at her feet, in the attitude of a petitioner. Janusz had brought in a wind-up gramophone and two scratched records – fruit of his wages for washing up at the Blenheim Arms. 'My friend sold me,' he said proudly, 'my washing friend. His name is Bright and he was a policeman. Now he is washing.'

Olga clapped her hands and kissed him on both cheeks. Now the Dance of the Polovtsian Maidens made conversation difficult, though it had certainly cheered up the party. Olga stamped her little feet, Posy and Janusz joined her. In the corner, Elenora, wearing what looked like second-hand rags, swayed to some other, inner tune.

'What did you say?' screeched Ilse. 'There's a nettle in my drink!'

'Give me back—'

'I can't hear a word. Speak up.'

'Ilse Lamprey, give me back my soul!'

'Don't be absurd, Mowle. What would I want with that? Babakov? Oh, Babakov isn't here, of course.'

'I beg you!'

'Mowle, you're a fool.' Ilse waved her hand. 'But if you believe I have the silly thing, take it. And if you are thinking of kissing my hand, don't.'

'God bless you, Ilse Lamprey.'

'And that's enough of that.'

If a miracle happened and a tear slid from Ilse Lamprey's eye, if she had in her own way, so far as she could, once loved Mowle just a little, no one noticed for Janusz had wound up the gramophone again, and in the centre of the small floor leaped into one of those uncomfortable-looking Russian knee-bending dances learned presumably in the course of his unfortunate sojourn at Murmansk. Olga sighed with joy at the merry turn her party was taking. Was that a thistle in the kettle from which she dispensed the drinks? No matter. One can live. One can be happy. She suddenly had a terrible feeling that the white liquid from the bottom of her bag was Max's surgical spirit. Never mind. Tonight she flung her pinny over the windmill and here to complete her happiness was the guest whose presence – next to Max's – she most missed.

Why had the music stopped?

'This noise! My patience is exhausted!'

Those eyes like dead coals, that voice from the charnel house, feeble but unmistakable. Olga saw why Janusz had stopped dancing, Posy had lifted the needle from the gramo-phone, Ilse's yellow face was white. Professor Mowle stepped back in horror, even Elenora shivered awake from whatever dream gripped her. Olga knew at last who Gruber was.

At the same moment the man with the withered left arm swayed in the doorway, there was a knock at the front door (Rainbird) and Ilse Lamprey spoke: 'Gruber!' she said. 'Go to your room!'

It was twenty minutes before anyone answered Rainbird's knocking and ringing and then a thin, rather rumpled-looking woman he faintly seemed to recognise opened the door a crack. Her voice was breathless and she appeared alarmed. All points to be noted and later added up.

'Good evening, madam. I have come to see a Miss E. Flitch.'

'I'm sorry, she's not available.'

'I fear I must see her whether or not she is available.'

'Can you tell me why?'

'It might be better, madam, if you were to open the door.'

Rainbird realised that he himself had been whispering back. The door was not even open wide enough to insert his foot.

'I'm sorry, I can't do that. Perhaps I could give Miss Flitch a message?'

'Official, Police. I deeply regret we have had no news of her cat.'

'A mistake. I'm sorry you have been troubled.'

Elenora, shaking, shut the door behind her and bolted it. From her wheelchair on the landing, Ilse Lamprey nodded.

Chapter Eleven

*O*f course it couldn't be him. In the flesh. It was this house of dreams and foreboding. Someone had called up his ghastly spirit. It was a joke. He was an imposter. A figment.

That was everyone's second thought after the initial shock. The third was that there could be no possible doubt. When the creature had gone to his room. When the hammering at the door and ringing of the bell had become impossible to ignore and Elenora (British passport) had been sent to answer it and returned. When they were all gathered again with the door bolted, when twilight hesitated on the edge of night, Ilse Lamprey spoke.

'I cannot ask you to disbelieve what you have just seen. All I can ask is your silence.

'Babakov, give me your hand.

'With three exceptions all of us in this room depend upon silence for our continued existence at 161 Radpole Road. The displaced must make themselves small and secret. Our life here, so painfully won, endowed by the man you have just seen, is too fragile for scandal. One day I may tell you a story which is not, after all, so fantastic. Man is a poor thing. Villains are simply dreamers to whom history has granted the opportunity to act. On one point I can reassure you – he is as harmless now as a new-born babe. He is out of history.

'Babakov. Take me downstairs. I am tired.'

'Babakov? Are you still there?'
'Ilse Lamprey?'

'Bring me the pad. And my pen.'

'You should sleep.'

'Time enough for that. I wonder, ought I to have warned them about Vera. I should have realised who she was. But who would have believed that Geli Raubal had a daughter? Who nowadays even recalls Geli Raubal? You won't remember all that, of course.'

Babakov would have been happier to hear no more of the subject. He gave as little thought as possible to the means of his rescue and flight from Berlin; also he had something else on his mind.

All the same he had the habit of obedience to Ilse Lamprey and tonight there was something about her that worried him: fragility? He brought her writing equipment and the extra-firm neck pillow she used for working in bed, drew the curtains, turned on the bedside light and sat down beside her. She took off her wig, handed it to Babakov.

'Geli Raubal?' he prompted.

'Ah yes.' She gestured for one of her thin black cigars then seemed to forget she was holding it. 'Well.' At last Ilse allowed the cigar to be lit and sank back against her pillow. 'I may not have told you, that is how I got mixed up with the whole boiling of them. Her mother, Angela Raubal, was Schicklgruber's half-sister, of course. I knew her in Obersalzberg when she was his housekeeper at the Haus Wachenfeld and Geli was twenty. She was a beauty, I can tell you. Cheerful too and a nice little voice. Here, put this scarf over the lampshade. It's blinding me.

'Where was I? Oh yes. Well, I moved to München about the same time he had set her up in the Prinzregentenstrasse. By then she was virtually a prisoner. Then there was the suicide business, though myself I'd put my money on that ferret Himmler. Heidler, Schicklgruber, whatever you like to call him, adored her. Such a fuss when she died – he even became a vegetarian. I think very little of love, as you know, but the man was quite out of his head for Geli. Yet I believe he had her killed. Nasty little Heinrich would never have dared, not without orders.'

'But if he loved her—'

'Gossip. You know I never listen.'

'Of course, Ilse Lamprey.'

'Well, there was a story, something about a baby. While our Führer-to-be could support the idea of marrying his own niece, a child would have been a most damaging embarrassment. As I heard it, a girl baby was born in 1930 and against Geli's wishes put in an orphanage in Wien under another name. In the final quarrel before her death Geli was begging to go to Wien not for her singing lessons but to see her daughter. If she threatened to reveal the child's existence, how could she be allowed to live? One can see it: the tears of rage, the faithful assassin, the hysterical remorse. Angela once showed me the shrine he made of Geli's room at Obersalzberg. By then he was Chancellor and I was a secretary but that is a story for another day. Or one to forget.' Ilse sighed. 'Oh, Babakov, how I long to forget. What was that noise?'

'The wind.'

'Something else. On the roof. A tile?'

'In the morning I shall look.'

'My poor true Babakov, have I treated you badly?'

'You saved my life, Ilse Lamprey.'

'Yes. That.'

'Do you know – was there evidence?'

'Rumours of a letter, I think. But I don't remember.' Babakov scratched his chin.

'So Vera is Geli's daughter? And his?'

The thought of Vera reminded him of the other thing he had on his mind he would have liked very much to hand over to someone else.

'I am convinced of it. I realise now I had been expecting her, yet when she arrived I did not know her.'

'Can we get rid of her?'

121

'Impossible. She is too dangerous. Clearly she is black-mailing the old man for the gold that is rightfully ours. What did you find in her room tonight?'

'Elenora Flitch's cat. The remains.'

'Well, I know that.' Ilse's snappishness had come back. 'What else?'

'Terrible things. Bones. And fur.'

'I am not surprised. For the moment you will speak of this to no one else. I shall have to think for everyone, as usual. That wind. I hate wind. Is the window bolted? Ah, Babakov, you have no idea how weary I am. That was surely too noisy for a tile?'

'A branch no doubt. I shall see to it in the morning. Shall I turn off the light?'

'Certainly not. Pass my spectacles. Wait, Babakov. Hold my hand. For a moment. There. That's better. Thank you, you may go to bed.'

As Babakov – exhausted by such a gale of events and confessions and reminders of days when the strong wind of history blew through his bones and all but uprooted him, flung him away – first visited Elenora, then lay down on his bed fully dressed but for his shoes, and Shadow patted his closed lids, claws sheathed, Ilse took the scarf off the lamp and began to write.

I, known as Ilse Lamprey, do attest for history the events here written to be true, so far as truth is ever possible. To this I give my last strength.

'Sergeant!'

It was too windy for gardening so Valerie Mowle had been sitting in the kitchen in her nightie polishing her competition, Queen for a Day, when Rainbird appeared at the back door.

'Down, Cuffy. Mr Rainbird, are you all right? Have you hurt your leg? You don't look very well. I think you work too hard. You should get more sleep. Oh, your poor ankle is quite swollen!'

Indoors in the light, he had quite a queer glint in his eye. If she didn't know better, Valerie would have imagined him to be drunk.

'Just a slip off a roof, madam. All in a night's work.'

'You poor man! A cold compress. Or is it hot? Or cold then hot? Or hot then cold?'

'No matter, Mrs Mowle. A rag will do. You see before you a man at the crown of his career.'

'Oh. I'm so glad.'

'If I told you what I have seen tonight.'

'Please do.' *Woman's Weekly* always said you must ask men about themselves even if the answers were boring.

'Between ourselves then, I have seen with my own eyes the greatest villain of our times.'

'Not the rapist of Radpole Road?'

'Worse than that. Much worse.'

The extraordinary thing about the indisputable horror was its unreality. That is, when they had listened to Ilse Lamprey and gone to their rooms and Gruber had retreated upstairs, they still found it difficult to credit what they had seen. There was no doubt and yet they could not believe. It was as though they had witnessed the most amazing conjuring trick.

Gathered by unspoken agreement in Elenora's room, at first none could think of anything to say and then they spoke in hushed voices. Posy made coffee which Janusz handed round with a little bow. Elenora sank back in her dove-blue chair, her hair all a-tangle, the widowed Aeneas settled comfortably on her lap. He who should have been bereaved seemed, if not actually joyous, at least complacent. With horror that made her gasp, she recalled Babakov's awful discovery. It struck Elenora what exactly had happened to poor Dido. She remembered Vera's tempting snacks and shuddered.

Gustavus Mowle – to his credit – was not one of nature's chairmen yet something seemed to be expected of him so he supposed he must be the first to speak the name.

'If we are to believe that Adolf Hitler is living in the attic of this house—'

'Oh no, surely not!' cried Olga, her scarves fallen and her ostrich feather drooping oddly over one eye. 'Such a sad old man. It is no joke growing old.'

'You have seen with your own eyes.'

'Yes. Alas.'

'Then we must be agreed. Whatever happens we must agree.'

'It is history,' said Olga, close to tears, 'we can never shake it off. It rides us. The Russians said he was dead but who can believe them?'

Posy and Janusz sat on the floor against the wall hand-in-hand, wide-eyed.

Gustavus wagged his head, weary from so much feeling in one evening. He thought with the nostalgia of one who has lost something forever of the peace of being English: rain on green fields and the certainty that one was always right. How had everything changed so suddenly? He was tired but realised that he was afraid to close his eyes for fear of what dreams might come.

'It is clear enough what we should do. Though I must admit I find it hard to imagine myself telephoning the police. Or rather, I can't imagine them believing me. Even if they did—'

He shuddered at the thought of the consequences. Publicity. Headlines. Embarrassment. The college would not like it at all. As for the university. He could see it now in one of those lurid Sunday papers Valerie took for the horoscopes: English prof nabs Adolf. He wondered vaguely how many crimes went undetected thanks to the national habit of looking the other way (in that respect Chamberlain was not so much a vacillating coward as an upright Englishman with all the natural reflexes).

Of course, such a monster should be brought to book. The odd thing was how a demon on such a scale became a phantasm. He who frightened children in their sleep

124

was in the flesh as hard to credit as a real Father Christmas.

Besides, more judicial death could not wake the millions, wash away the tide of blood. To jog the memory of the world? Would that even be kind?

And Ilse would lose her home. And the Countess, and Babakov and Janusz Grzyb.

'Does anyone have anything to say? Miss Flitch? Elenora?'

Elenora's eyes were wild violets opening, thought Gustavus – perhaps there was something after all in the kind of literary clichés to which Valerie was so devoted. Her voice, however, though faint, was remarkably firm.

'Silence,' said Elenora. 'What Ilse Lamprey asks. It's not so difficult. All we have to do is to go on living as we were. Change is the difficult thing. Very difficult indeed.'

'And now we must sleep upon it,' Olga announced, almost herself again. 'Tomorrow is always another day. Ah, Posy, good night dear girl. And Janusz, darling boy.'

By midnight Posy was curled against Janusz's hairless chest. Already what she had seen that night had dissolved almost into a bad dream that daylight would surely banish.

What was that sound, like feet on gravel?

Just the wind, that was all. The wind.

While Ilse wrote and Posy slept as comfortable as a spoon, Vera circled the house in rage. Bolted against her! At last she found Rainbird's ladder still propped against the roof and for the second time that night the man with the eyes of coal looked up at his skylight in horror.

If forgetfulness is innocence Dr Gruber was almost blameless. The face of the man with the eyebrows that met across the middle had frightened him, appearing like that at the skylight. He had been by no means happy to let in Vera though he knew he had no choice and tonight at least she seemed not disposed to linger.

He had been puzzled by the reaction when he had gone downstairs to complain quite reasonably about the noise that made his skull ache, as did the wind now, rattling the tiles of the shallow roof that stood between him and everlasting night. Stretched on his bed, he looked up at the skylight that had earlier framed Rainbird's face with its expression first of triumph then of alarm as it abruptly vanished, to be followed by the sound of something heavy thumping and scrabbling for a hold.

As he lay, Dr Gruber's agitation diminished. Some wayward mercy – or fathomless exhaustion or perhaps his self-imposed starvation diet – had bestowed upon him the blessing of a ragged, quirkish memory that approached at times amnesia. He was aware as a child might be of certain things that disturbed his immediate comfort – tonight, for instance, that racket downstairs – but already Rainbird's face was fading and along with it the terror.

Even Vera's identity from time to time slipped his mind and if he turned off the lamp and lit his candle the crowding ghosts that used to persecute him, to scream from the flames for revenge, the hulking figures of those who had smiled and betrayed him, his disappointed hopes, his fervent powerful years – all were dissolved and in their place little scraps of happiness returned.

'*Mutter?*' he murmured and there she was with an extra blanket, a goose-feather pillow. Downy soft were those days. The boy at the end of youth. Urfahr, Linz, Wien. Music. Dreams. A flowering meadow, a girl riding a white steed. Geli? No. That was when he was young, his first love: Stephanie.

A hole in the hard December earth at Leonding. Mother gone. Don't look.

Are you there, Geli? Don't go. I'm cold. Blow out the candle. Let's sleep.

If history could not forget him, then he would forget history.

Chapter Twelve

At the top of the world insensate Everest remained indifferent to the midgets attempting to scale her. They were well above the waist now and the shining summit was intermittently visible.

Ilse Lamprey read and tossed the newspaper aside. We could have been angels, she thought. How did we fall so low? If there were a God, which there isn't, he must be drunk.

If there were a God's eye view, what would he make of the creatures that move upon the earth and the deep? Pity? Disappointment?

Yet we go on, we struggle, as if it mattered. I can see. It is amazing how much I can see. If I close my eyes I can ride the winds on my broomstick, though it is given to me to change nothing. Merely to record. Useless visions.

Upon the surface of the earth there was indeed movement, as Rainbird – having decided to bypass the Super – journeyed once more along the Paddington line, his destination Scotland Yard or it might even be Whitehall. His ankle hurt but his head was in clouds of glory. Justification! Commendation! Valerie Mowle!

Other signs of life. An English Queen prepared for anointing at the orifices, a Russian bomb for testing. At the Convent of the Little Flowers of St Anne, a novice hanging out the washing and humming as she pegged, with one eye for a thunderbolt (the novice mistress) and another for rain.

At Paddington Green police station, Inspector Fox assembled once again the evidence in the Viaduct Murder. Small toothmarks. Female. Query? Female person seen with victim in station buffet some hours previous. Noted only for grey cloak, texture of blanket. Scraps of grey wool beneath victim's fingernails. Let the mind rove. Inspiration came best when uncalled-for. Fox blew on his tea. He shuffled the routine bulletins for all stops on the Paddington line and picked one at random. His eyes opened wide. No less than one hundred missing cats in less than three months. Modus operandi common to the half dozen recovered corpses. He was a dog man himself but all the same . . .

O Christus Domine! sang the novice putting a last peg in Sister Michael's long johns. One can, after all, thought Mother Martin, believe in angels, if only for five blessed minutes. Which called to her mind Elenora Flitch who, in repose, reminded her of some angelic face she had forgotten. Rome, Florence, Venice? Leonardo? Giotto? She remembered the warning of her own novice mistress against art, against the facsimile of beauty which was not to be taken as a picture of the soul. In that respect she had secretly rebelled. And so now could find joy in the clear small voice of the laundry novice in the morning garden. She hoped there would be singing in heaven.

While Mother Martin was contemplating beauty and Elenora, Gustavus was trying to open his umbrella and considering Elenora. Or more particularly, his soul; which he would have liked to wrap up in tissue paper (since Ilse Lamprey had returned it) and give to Elenora. But the timing – in view of recent events and a certain wildness about Elenora – seemed inappropriate. Besides, ever since

128

Ilse Lamprey returned it he had begun to wonder if he had a soul at all. He didn't *feel* restored. He felt exactly as he had for years. The same face looked back from the shaving mirror. The same disorganised, unpublished, undistinguished, uncoordinated figure made his daily escape from his wife and her dog; though looking at Valerie – which he did as little as possible – she at least did seem different in some way Gustavus found hard to pin down. Smug? Pleased with herself? Preoccupied? Almost, he would have said, *happy*.

Not that Gustavus grudged her that. He had met her firewatching (some eccentricity of his inner ear had kept him out of the war, which suited him though gave him a tendency to topple at sea) and proposed to her by mistake on a train. That is to say, out of his profound shyness he had passed a remark now forgotten which she had misheard as a proposal. Or so it appeared when they had changed trains at Didcot and found themselves alone in the compartment and Gustavus, to his alarm, in Valerie's ample arms, smothered, engaged, horrified. In the same frame of mind he had married her and stayed with her ever since (though dining as often as possible in college).

From the top deck of the bus (yes, it was raining) Gustavus looked down into the Convent garden where a pretty young nun was snatching clothes from the line, stuffing pegs into her mouth. Perhaps he should have become a monk? Certainly he seemed to bring little happiness to anyone.

His infatuation with Ilse Lamprey could, he supposed, be explained by the same weakness of character that brought now to his mind visions of whitewashed cells, celibacy and silence. To worship Ilse had been safe, a liaison that could never be, a fantasy that would remain securely a fantasy.

Which brought Gustavus, standing now in the rain in the characteristic stance of a heron studying the pavement for fish, to the question of Elenora Flitch for whom a very peculiar feeling he had never known before had been growing. Swelling, you could say. Another fantasy? Or could it be love?

Bowled off the pavement by a woman pushing a pram, Gustavus stood in the running gutter and in apology raised a hat he was not wearing. He had left his umbrella on the bus.

Only in college did Gustavus remember the purpose of his trip to town. He could ask, of course: this university – his own college indeed – sheltered almost every living authority on almost every subject from the Rosetta stone to the mating habits of the snail. To ask though might be to arouse curiosity. Instead Gustavus squelched his way across the library, paused at the card index and made his way through the stacks to the sparse modern history shelf. Nothing much after the Treaty of Versailles. Ah, here it was under World War Second: Hitler A.

Every jolt was searing agony in his ankle but all the same Rainbird peg-legged around London. His reception on the whole had been gratifying – he had almost felt that he was expected. And now in a very top office indeed, he laid out his evidence: the first scrap of paper that had led him to investigate 161 Radpole Road, other documents including the copy of a certain letter extracted with menaces from the family of the Hieronymite Catholic priest, deceased, and finally a report (eye-witnessed by himself) on the illegal immigrant in the attic of Radpole Road. Even to think of it brought his ankle on again but what was triumph without pain?

'Perhaps if you would step this way, Detective Sergeant?'

They gave nothing away here at the top. Carpet on the floor. Nice manners. Nothing cheeky. When they jabbed the needle into his arm, Rainbird was still smiling.

'I have the proof!'

Vera was angry. Ilse Lamprey looked up and rubbed her

130

eyes. She had been writing all night. She had been in another country. As she wrote the phantasms faded from the garden and she felt the coldness in her bones. The fog of death rising? The circus, the dancing bears, the party guests all gone and in their place Vera was shaking with rage. She had donned again the grey cloak in which she had arrived. What very sharp teeth! What a pointed nose!

'Someone was in my room last night.'

'So?'

She could strangle me in my bed, thought Ilse. That is not my plan. That would not do at all. She measured the distance from the bed to the bell-pull. Not that old Babakov could climb more than a couple of stairs before I too became a figment. Or whatever it is the dead become. If only the girl would stand still.

'What are you writing?'

'History.'

Vera looked sceptical. She studied with scornful interest the arrangement of pulleys over Ilse's bed. There was no room in her world for cripples.

'What for?'

'So that I can forget it.'

Mentally Ilse sketched in a black moustache on Vera's upper lip and wiped it off again. But there was something about the nose and the eyes and certainly about the temperament. Geli was less easily discernible. Vera was neither blonde nor pretty, though when she had been on one of her spending sprees at Colliers' she did have an air. Hardly a honeypot like her mother, but striking enough to turn heads.

'What's this machinery for?'

'So that I can get out of bed.'

'I don't know why you bother.'

Is there such a thing, Ilse wondered, as pure evil? Only such a short time ago the idea might have appealed to her. Something had changed. She did not care very much for the alteration but was beginning to accept it. Acceptance?

Not a word to which she was accustomed, it was much too close to resignation, old folks' homes, bibs and feeding mugs, and she was by no means ready for that.

'History's a lie,' Vera announced. 'Every time there's a war the politicians alter it.'

'So you are a lie?'

Ha, that made the young madam sit up.

'What do you mean? I am an irrefutable fact.'

Ilse nodded.

'You are his daughter. The man we call Gruber.'

'Yes, of course. How do you know?'

'I guessed.'

'So that gold is mine. He wouldn't give it to me. He went crazy. He seemed to think I was a ghost.'

'You are in a way. So are we all. Since officially we never entered this country we do not exist. A house of ghosts.'

'I can wait. He'll have to give way in the end. I have the Stempfle letter. When I didn't know who I was – when I had forgotten – I had no idea what it meant. My mother left it to me. It was in a bank in Bavaria.'

'But Stempfle was killed. The letter destroyed.'

'That was a copy. There are others – I have several. But I have the original. It was my birthright, my birth certificate you might say. Do you want one? I thought so. There you are.'

Ilse felt suddenly drained. She wanted to flap her hands at the girl: go, go, take your filthy shadows with you back to hell.

All the same, when Vera had left, Ilse reached for the paper the girl had tossed on the bed. When she had read it she lay back on her pillows, grey, and reached for the bell-pull.

In the library Gustavus was reading with equal intensity and an almost equal sense of alarm. It was the gap that worried him.

Witness Fräulein Manzialy, the Führer's vegetarian

132

cook, April 29th, 1945, the marriage in the bunker. Witness Frau Gertrude Junge, secretary, will dictated making provision for surviving relatives to maintain 'petty-bourgeois' standard of living. At three thirty p.m. the sound of the gunshot. Witness valet SS Sturmbannführer, body burned in shell hole: 'his black trousers and shoes protruded from the army field grey blanket'. And then nothing. No bones. Not a whisper. But surely the Russians? What was this? Rumours of a hoard of gold never recovered. As far as history was concerned for all but his victims the slate was wiped clean. But what if? By teatime Gustavus's head ached. In the Kardomah he took off his spectacles and closed his eyes but even then there was no escape. The monstrous face of the twentieth century's nightmare merged with that of an old man with a withered arm, framed in the Countess's doorway. And Elenora was there, in that house!

'Put in your teeth, Gruber, we're all in the same boat,' said Ilse Lamprey.

The lodger in the attic had refused to come down so with considerable difficulty Babakov had carried her up the last, narrow flight of stairs.

At first Gruber had refused to acknowledge her presence. He lay there, his thumb in his mouth, his mind, if anywhere, on something more *gemütlich* than reality in the shape of Ilse Lamprey. Then something she was saying shocked him into wavering attention.

'The Stempfle letter.'

'I have been forced to eat offal,' he whimpered.

'Never mind that.'

The old man lay back, staring at the ceiling. If he could not see Ilse Lamprey, she might go away. Maybe the skylight which reminded him of Rainbird jogged his ragged memory.

'I am misjudged by history. The assassins are come to claim me.'

133

'Rubbish. If you feel like that you should have gone to Argentina in the first place.'

He turned his head. Ilse thought, he really is frightened. A bit mad, very frightened.

'Who is that?' He pointed a shaking finger. 'My executioner?'

'That's Babakov. You know perfectly well who he is. You are the monster here but unfortunately we have no choice but to protect you.' Ilse sighed. 'You remember Bernhard Stempfle? The priest of the Hieronymite order?'

'Another traitor!'

'That's as may be. His neck was broken anyway, if I remember correctly, in the forest of Harlaching. The point is, he was one of the few who knew about your mésalliance with Geli Raubal. A compromising letter from you to her fell into the wrong hands. Stempfle retrieved it, doubtless with party money. The rumour was that in it you confessed to your masochistic sexual inclinations, which interest me not at all. What does concern me is a reference – in your characteristically hysterical vein – to the fact that Geli was pregnant: *schwanger*. I had long suspected this. As you know, I was close to her mother, in 1929 I was living in München.'

'I let the child live! I gave way against my better judgment!'

'Ah I see your memory's coming back. You wish to see the letter? I have it here. Or shall I read it to you?'

Ilse put on her spectacles. She held the paper by the corner, with distaste.

'". . . the child is out of the question. In the name of our love I demand that you dispose of it." And more on the same theme. But she didn't, did she?'

'Give me that letter!'

'By all means. Tear it up if you like. It's only a copy.'

Gruber stood, shakily. His raging shadow seemed to fill the small room. Babakov backed towards the door.

'I let her live – I let the child live! Geli begged me. I could deny her nothing.'

Ilse nodded. 'And she was put in an orphanage in Wien. You never saw her, you never acknowledged her. But we know her name, don't we? The name of the person who holds the original of this letter? The one you had imagined dead?'

The shadow shrank. The voice was a furious whisper. 'Vera.'

'Yes. So. You realise the implications for all of us?'

'How can we get rid of her?'

'Not so easy. She is her father's daughter. Perhaps a little of the gold with enough left over for the housekeeping?'

'It is almost exhausted. She has taken so much.'

'I see. Well, I suppose we'll manage somehow. I believe the Countess has diamonds. But we must be careful. The letter itself is not of so much account. Vera is. She would take pleasure in betraying us. Babakov! You may carry me downstairs.'

His visitors gone, the man known as Gruber curled in a foetal position into the corner of his bed where the attic ceiling was lowest. He sucked his knuckles and whimpered, longing for the forgetfulness that had soothed and rocked him before Ilse Lamprey interrupted. He squeezed his eyes tight shut and pulled the blanket over his head. If he made himself very small, almost invisible, perhaps they would not find him. Perhaps he might even cease to exist. Perhaps they would come again, those kinder shades.

Back in her room, Ilse allowed Babakov to settle her in bed. Daft old thing, he'd been quite scared in the attic. Well, it had hardly been a party for any of them.

'His mother loved him, you know.'

Babakov nodded heavily.

'I suppose everyone has a mother. Even him.'

'We owed him something. But we can take the debt as paid. I wonder whether to believe him about the gold.'

135

'You will be right, Ilse Lamprey. As always.'

'I think we have earned a little English noggin. Babakov, get the bottle.'

'The Christmas vodka?'

'Why not.'

Half an hour and half a bottle later, Babakov felt his eyelids drooping.

'You will not work today?'

He hoped for his dismissal.

'You may go but I must work. Until today I had known. Now I am certain. I must get it all down.'

'All?'

'Yes. I shall put down everything. Nothing will be left out.'

Oh, the bodikins, the corseleting, the horsehair, the paint and the golden shoes that pinched!

In the drill hall behind the Britannia, Elenora was fitted for her role. While Posy Clamp pinned her hem she looked at the cold white face of the Virgin Queen, served like a cutlet in a ruffle, and wondered whatever she was doing here and who was that woman in the mirror.

'Ouch.'

'Gosh. I'm sorry, Miss Flitch.'

Elenora was growing accustomed to bewilderment in the face of mirrors. She no longer knew herself and would not have been surprised to get up one morning and find no reflection at all. In the streets she had a sense of invisibility, as if no one could see her or she could walk through people. She had taken to walking very fast. She avoided glancing in shop windows (mirrors again) for fear of what she might not see. Was that what love was all about? Someone to show you who you are? She opened her mouth to ask Posy and closed it again.

On the bus in the dark in the rain on the way back to Radpole Road, it suddenly struck Elenora that somewhere in the course of all the dizzying events and sensations of the last few days, she had lost something: the voice of coarse lust that had so embarrassed her and got her into bed with the wretched Sproke. Well, that was a relief.

For the first time in weeks, it seemed, Elenora smiled as she opened the door of Radpole Road.

'Hello, Babakov. Oh, we have to lock the door behind us, don't we. I'd nearly forgotten.'

'The Professor was asking for you, Miss Flitch. He's just gone. I thought he seemed worried.'

As the widowed Aeneas rushed to meet her, Elenora smiled again. Gustavus Mowle, indeed. Well, fancy that.

Chapter Thirteen

*R*adpole Road held its terrible secret but the world whizzed on. The thin sun shone. After the rain the birds had come out on the bough again, their song even sweeter. The philadelphus would be in bloom in time to dress Gloriana's barge borrowed from the rowing club and towed up-river to the ferry crossing at the end of Radpole Road. The university girls too had come out in their summer dresses and cardigans in case, tulips gathered around their bicycles in bunches, nodding their pretty heads, eyes bright for the boys.

In the Convent garden Elenora watched Aeneas pick his way with high paws through the dew. The murmur of prayer from the chapel. The first bumble bee. Yes, she thought, for the time, this is right.

She had spoken to only two people.

Dame Hilda had been understanding. Just what she would have recommended. A little sick leave. Elenora's tutorials would be delegated. Very lowering, these summer colds.

'A short retreat?' Mother Martin had said. 'Well yes, that is a different matter. I see no reason why not. Will you require silence?'

'Oh, I don't think so,' said Elenora. She sounded to Mother Martin tired but less hysterical. One could only hope there would be no hellish emissaries slithering up the path in Elenora's train. 'If I could bring my cat? Aeneas has had rather a bad time lately.'

'Naturally. Anything else?'

'Just a cell. And a little peace.'

'I'm sure we can manage that.'

Valerie Mowle nipped out to post her contribution to *Woman's Home*. She had never won anything and assumed she was unlikely to start now. All the same she had enjoyed being Queen for a Day.

On the way to the box she noticed that it was quite a nice morning for people who like mornings. Then it struck her – there had been something missing the last few days, something she had grown used to, comfortable with (almost like her friend): the policeman whose eyebrows met across the middle.

'And how are we today then? This beautiful morning?'

Rainbird opened one eye then the other. After a minute he remembered who he was. How he was a different matter. The light was too bright and though his feet seemed to be attached still to his legs he didn't feel so sure about his toes and his mouth tasted like a Turkish wrestler's jock-strap.

'Crocked.'

'Well, we're in the right place for that. Better in no time, you'll see. Now then, let's be a good boy and just pop this in.'

The figure shaking down the thermometer wore a nurse's uniform but was not Rainbird's idea of a nurse. It, or rather he, was six foot tall in his plimsolls and looked as though he could do with a shave. Before Rainbird could protest he was having his temperature taken.

'Naughty now! Don't try to talk.'

The Detective Sergeant groaned and closed his eyes. He felt a prick in his arm and two minutes later – or it might have been two hours or two days – a voice spoke from a great distance.

'Herbert?'

No one since his granny had called him Herbert. She had those striped gobstoppers in a tin with a picture of a Beefeater and smelled of puddings.

'Granny?'

She had a black whisker in her chin but Herbert didn't mind.

'You've been having horrid dreams, haven't you, Herbert? About a nasty man?'

Rainbird struggled but he couldn't raise his head. He had the impression of a big eye staring at him down a narrow tunnel. His own voice seemed to be somebody else's.

'I saw the nasty man. I climbed on the roof and I saw him.'

Another prick, this time in his buttock, and Rainbird saw someone – himself – running away, a tiny little fat man, down the tunnel and the tunnel got narrower and narrower.

Elsewhere, in a carpeted room very close to the Top, a meeting was taking place. The sun shone on Horseguards Parade, on the spires and towers of Westminster and Whitehall, on the leafy Mall where preparations were almost complete for the coming of the Queen, on London pigeons precariously copulating on the windowsills of power.

'Quick thinking, Hugo.'

'I'd put out the word. He was simply passed on, so to speak. His Superintendent thought he'd warned him off but apparently not. Then in he comes and drops it in my lap. Remarkable material, I must say. And he'd seen him with his own eyes.'

'A.H.?'

'Himself. In the attic of the house in Radpole Road.'

'Mmn. Must have given our Sergeant Rainbird quite a turn.'

'On the contrary. He'd been on his track for some time.'

'And the security aspect?'

'If the Lamprey woman or any of the illegals were going to talk they'd have done so long ago. Not in their interest. And they've got Rainbird down at the Park for a bit of a brain-scrape. The Spring-cleaners do a good job.'

'Indeed. Oh, thank you, Hugo, just a splash. It is midday. I suppose we have done the right thing?'

'No question at all. Think of the alternative. Coronation jamboree and up pops the Great Dictator living in England. Set us back years. Gift to the Commies, embarrassment to our pals the Germans and the Jews would never believe us.'

'Believe what?'

'That we didn't know he'd been here all the time.'

'Did we?'

In a much smaller room in the capital Inspector Fox of Paddington Green police station was on the telephone. In front of him was the file on the Viaduct Murder. Always best to have a contact. What was the name? At the police pantomine the year before last? Birdog?

'Perhaps you'd get him to call me?'

'I'm afraid that's not possible.'

'When he comes in?'

'Detective Sergeant Rainbird has disappeared.'

'Disappeared? Miss Flitch? But this is most inconvenient. We have the last rehearsal for the pageant. She is our Gloriana.'

Babakov looked at the telephone. He had never liked telephones because of the electricity. He held it as far away as he could. Then he put it down.

Mowle, thought Ilse Lamprey who had called the meeting, looked a wreck. If he had his soul back it seemed not to have done him much good.

'Here we all are then.' All who had attended Olga's fateful party: Janusz, Posy, the Countess, Babakov, Mowle and Ilse herself. 'Except for Miss Flitch. Has anyone seen Miss Flitch? Babakov?'

'She has disappeared, Ilse Lamprey. And her cat.'

Ilse nodded. 'A lover, I daresay. Are you all right, Mowle? You look pale. Good. Well, I have brought us together to decide what is to be done. I have come to my own conclusion. I have been working very hard – it is tiring remembering – so I should be glad to keep this short. Does anyone have anything to say? Countess?'

Olga seemed to have shrunk. She gave the appearance of a small bird with straws in its feathers and a bald patch on top. She felt as though she had left her common sense somewhere and had forgotten where she had put it. If only she had not conceived the idea of a birthday party! And she still had no idea whose birthday it had been. Was it her own? Surely not. Each year she wrapped Max's last present and gave it to herself, so it couldn't have been. She shook her head.

As usual, Janusz and Posy held hands. Pointless to ask lovers, Ilse concluded, might just as well hold a conversation with a sparrow. She knew Babakov would think what he was told to think so there remained only the Professor.

'Mowle?'

'I'm sorry?'

Ilse's eyes snapped. She was wearing – perhaps for the last time – her black wig, bow-tie and bottle-green smoking jacket.

'Apparently everything is left up to me, as usual. In my opinion once a fiend always a fiend – people don't change you know, or not very much. But he has more to lose from disclosure than anyone in this house. Only one threat remains and there is only one way to deal with it.' Ilse paused, not for effect but from the sleeplessness of writing nights; her strength was ebbing, it would have been easy to wave them all away – the living were little more substantial than the dead.

'The girl Vera,' she said. 'And for her there is one answer. Death.'

Not merely to save ourselves – Ilse wrote later – but because she is the child of the most terrible phantom of our times. Devil's spawn. Not that I believe in the devil or anything else much. But the word will serve well enough. Just as those who have not the courage to grow up give the name God to their need for an immortal father, so Lucifer will do for the naive too self-deceiving to acknowledge man's infinite capacity for behaving badly. (Oh, well, call it wickedness if you will. What's in a word.) Genetic inheritance seems to me, on the other hand, a perfectly sensible concept. Also the matter of conditioning. If the customs officer had been a kinder father, the mother not died. If the young A.H. had been accepted by the Academy of Fine Arts.

If Vera had not been cast as she was into an orphanage she might even have shunned the command of her genes, though of that I am not so sure. The only certainty is that she cannot be allowed to run around the world.

The others reacted much as I expected. I shall have to tidy up, as ever.

When Ilse spoke the word, Olga's hands flew to her face in horror, even Posy gasped and Janusz too when Posy had explained what Ilse meant. Babakov groaned, wondering what part he would be required to play in whatever hideous plot Ilse Lamprey devised.

Only Gustavus Mowle barely reacted. First he had been frantic at the thought of Elenora in the same house as Gruber and his daughter. Now he was frantic at the thought that Elenora had disappeared. Slaughtered? Blissful in the arms of another man? One option seemed almost as fearful as the other.

So distracted he was a moment or two passed before he realised that the meeting had ended and he was alone with Ilse Lamprey, who was eyeing him as a sparrow-hawk might contemplate a vole.

'I'm so sorry, Ilse Lamprey, what did you say?'

'Mowle, you're in love.'

'Am I? Yes, I suppose I am. Yes, you're absolutely right. As ever.'

'Extraordinary.'

'What?'

'Love. Never had much to do with it myself. Is it painful?'

'Rather.'

'So I assumed. And observed.' Ilse glanced, thinking, not looking at the open window, a picture of summer. The birds shrieked. 'Tell me: does it make up for things?'

'Oh yes. Everything.'

In the absence of Detective Sergeant Rainbird the Superintendent had reinstated PC Bright. Apart from dishpan hands, Bright had quite enjoyed himself washing up at the Blenheim Arms. Janusz Grzyb had been good enough company and interesting on the subject of 161 Radpole Road. Bright being Bright, it had been no time before he had mapped out for himself a future in the most glittering halls of catering.

This was better though. Back at his desk with every possibility of early promotion if Rainbird, his tormentor, continued to be disappeared. He had had several conversations with Inspector Fox of Paddington Green and was already contemplating an outstanding career in the Metropolitan. Detective Inspector Bright, Superintendent Bright, Commissioner Bright. Commissioner and Mrs Bright. Her Majesty commands the presence of Commissioner Sir Arnold and Lady Bright. A firm handshake from the Duke, a manly pat on the back? It was nothing, sir, thank you, ma'am.

In the absence of Elenora Flitch, the chairman and helpers on the University Coronation committee were almost as distraught as Gustavus Mowle. Stand-ins were tried out but it was a matter not only of Gloriana but Cinderella. The shoes did not fit, nor did anything else. Without their true Gloriana, Belphoebe, Una, Britomart, Mercilla all in the one slim frame, the unthinkable was possible. Reason might fall to Chaos, Gown lose out to Town.

*

144

'Have you noticed,' said Elenora to Mother Martin, 'how the birds go in and out? I have been watching the same tree for half an hour. When they go in you can't see a single feather, but such a racket. The collar-doves have nested in the lilac. Is it true they marry?'

'So they say.' Mother Martin was knitting a sweater for Father Clement. She was having trouble with the fisherman's knots. What would Father Clement want knots for, anyway? Perhaps she could fall back on rib with just a single cable up the front. She glanced at Elenora. Not quite stable yet, she suspected, but different, certainly. She was about to add that doves have a very small intelligence but thought better of it. Fey was not a word she cared to apply to her friend whose intellect she had always respected. She settled for fragile, in the convalescent sense. As one might speak of someone who has been through an ordeal, is getting better but to a stranger would still look in need of Parrish's Food, plenty of milk and a good rest.

To her relief Elenora was clearly not asking for permanent sanctuary. Nor was there any more talk of wraiths from hell. She brought with her no little horned devils, only the cat who enchanted the novices and was no trouble at all.

'Is Aeneas quite well? I've noticed he runs away from Sister Michael. I suppose it's the boots.'

'He has been through a bad time.'

'So have you, my dear, I think?'

'Yes, I have, rather.' Elenora smiled absently and touched the silver pendant at her throat. 'But I'm much better now. Whatever it was, it just went away. I can't explain. That's funny – I always used to feel that everything had to be explained. And if it couldn't be, then it was dangerous. I've only just realised that. Is it the same with faith – your kind of faith, I mean – doing without explanations?'

Mother Martin laid down her knitting.

'Yes. In the beginning it can be quite difficult. Then you don't need them any more.'

'But the really terrible things—'

'Those are acts of man, not God.'

'You make it sound so simple.'

Although her sequestration lasted only a few days it felt longer to Elenora, in the way of recovery, understanding and quiet happiness. She sewed, watched television in Mother Martin's parlour, helped in the kitchen, avoided Sister Michael whose presence reminded her of the duties she was neglecting. She found an old white muslin shift in the bag she had packed in the flurry of leaving Radpole Road, washed it and wore it to hoe the vegetable garden. Once or twice when the chapel was empty she sat there. She could not pray but it was calming for she felt the air to be full of prayers, like the pure white handkerchiefs on the Convent washing-line.

Not that Valerie Mowle was worried. Exactly. All the same. You get used to people and she had been lonely for a long time. She looked at the telephone. There was Cuffy, of course but, alas, probably not for long now and in the eighth month of her phantom pregnancy Valerie felt her solitude more than usual. Her friend had been around hardly at all and then only bits of Her and not Her whole attention. Gustavus never seemed to be in for more than five minutes but even if he had been there he wouldn't have been. He never had been altogether there all through their marriage and that used to upset her until she realised, just lately, that he was not made for her nor she for him. What she needed was not a clever man but a nice ordinary man who sat down to his dinner in the middle of the day, took an annual week's holiday in a boarding house by the sea and had to watch his weight.

'Stop that at once, Cuffy,' said Valerie automatically.

'I'm sorry, madam?' At the other end of the telephone Bright sat upright, as he did for all calls.

Valerie explained her anxiety as well as she could. The young man's answer hardly set her mind at rest.

'Detective Sergeant Rainbird has gone on a long leave.'
Very long, Bright hoped. Could be for ever. Fingers crossed.

Down at the Park, Rainbird was allowed up and out for the first time. He asked for his clothes back but they said he would be better in a dressing-gown. They had explained: this was a rest home and he was getting on very well. Yes, if he felt up to it he could sit on a bench by himself for a while. They'd have another little chat a bit later.

Alone at last Rainbird recalled certain things. Something about his granny and a tunnel. Quite a lot was coming back – his name, his job, the smell of flannel. And then a gap as if someone had cut out a piece of his memory. One thing he knew, he'd never get it back till he was over that wall and out. What he had to decide was whether he wanted it back and how could he do that until he knew what it was?

From the top deck of the bus from Radpole Road into town Gustavus glanced down, over the wall of the Convent of the Little Flowers of St Anne. He looked and then looked again at the figure in white muslin standing like a figure engraved with a hoe in one hand and a dove at her feet.

Chapter Fourteen

*R*ainbird, now making his way by mentally purblind instinct in dressing-gown and slippers to the nearest station on the Paddington line, thought he had been in a rest home.

Gustavus thought Elenora Flitch had become a nun.

Vera thought she was getting weaker. Fainter. That is, less solid. She smelled something like ashes and realised it was she herself who carried this sulphurous odour. No amount of bathing or drenching with the scent she had bought at Colliers' with Gruber's gold would get rid of it. The grey cloak she had taken to wearing again was impregnated.

Just lately her mood swung unpredictably between rage and fear. One moment she felt she had it in her power to call up the winds of the universe, to shake this house to pieces; then she would swoop around the corridors, fly up the stairs, put eye and ear to keyholes, beat on her father's attic door. Not that she could see in that stinking old man the figure who had once done to the world what she would like to do to Radpole Road.

Then the next second Vera would be most terribly afraid. The house was plotting to destroy her or to banish her back into the shades from which she came. She locked her door, pulled the curtains and closed her eyes. It wasn't fair. Her mother was dead. She had a father. Fathers were supposed to love. She squatted in the corner, knees up to her chin and rocked herself from side to side. Vera sat in the corner and sucked her thumb.

England, London in particular, looked up. The weather was definitely dodgy for the Coronation. Valerie Mowle's friend on a flying visit put up Her feet for two seconds and confided.

'I do hope the going will be good.'

'For the coach?'

'For the horse. We have one running, you see.'

The first hopefuls were already camped out in the Mall with their groundsheets, sleeping bags, sandwiches, thermoses and packaway macs. Come wind or weather they would sit it out and the weather was on its way.

The clouds gathered and burst over Radpole Road and the university city. In St Jude's meadow the ready-heaped bonfires were covered with tarpaulin. The river rose and overflowed its banks but Gloriana's barge rode the swell, shuddering, groaning and bedecked. In the drill hall behind the Britannia where the committee and helpers gathered to warm and cheer themselves over dark brown tea, there was much discussion about the absence of the Virgin Queen. Really it was too bad of Miss Flitch – such a sensible woman.

In Mother Martin's parlour Elenora was learning to knit. She was finding it a comfortable thing to do on a rainy day though quite difficult at first until you got the hang.

'What lovely names,' she said. 'All Fool's Welt. Trellis Faggot! Falling Leaf. Oh dear, I've dropped a stitch.'

On the television a black-and-white person was giving a history of Westminster Abbey in a hushed voice. Then someone else came on and said the Queen would probably be wearing leeks. Then there was a picture of a man in a deckchair in the Mall giving a thumbs-up with one hand and waving the Union Flag with the other. He was wearing a dressing-gown and there was something about the way his eyebrows met across the middle that looked faintly familiar.

'I'd almost forgotten,' Elenora said. 'I'm supposed to be Gloriana. They must be terribly worried. Do you think I should?'

'If you feel up to it, my dear. If you promised.'

'Yes, I did.'

'Then you should.'

'It's so lovely here. I don't want to leave.'

That evening a parcel was delivered to the gatehouse addressed to Miss E. Flitch. Elenora took it in wonder. Who could know she was here? She opened the book, studied the inscription, blushed with surprise and began to read.

Wake, now my love, awake; for it is time

'Perhaps I will,' she said to Mother Martin. 'I suppose they're depending on me. You've been so kind. Thank you. I'd like you to have this back, it's too precious and I don't really need it any more.'

Mother Martin received the phial in the silver filigree pendant as reverently as though this truly were a tear of Christ. A tear pricked in her own eye as she locked it away. The powers of the Lord were wonderful but it was almost as remarkable what imagination could do for itself.

Elenora would leave in the morning. Meanwhile she slept in her white cell, her cat at her feet, the book in the University Press dark blue binding close to her heart.

In the attic of Radpole Road, Olga Rákosfalvi persuaded Gruber to take a mouthful of strained cabbage. She had had to buckle on her courage with her pinny to get herself up here and now, having arrived, she wondered what she had been frightened of. The smell in the low room was nothing more than that of unwashed man and age and sickness. She forced herself to sit down to make sure he ate.

150

'Good,' she said with a sprightliness she did not feel. 'And tomorrow perhaps a bath?'

Gruber blinked and looked at Olga as though trying to recognise her. She had an unnerving sensation of being looked not at but through, as if there were someone else standing behind her. He pulled his blanket around him, curled up again on the bed and seemed to be trying to speak. He beckoned her closer and she held her breath and tried to remember that a man is only a man after all when he has finished. Finished such terrible things. But what was the point of retribution without atonement? And – even if he knew what he had done – how in a millennium could any act of contrition be devised to match cruelties like that? He will never be shriven.

His whisper was foul in her ear but she had put up with worse than that in the bad years. He called her by names she did not know.

'Did you know, I dreamed of taking Holy Orders? At Lambach. I sang in the choir.'

'Hush.'

'What is that noise? Who is there?'

'Nothing. Just the rain.'

The Queen anointed, the ritual done, three times they had cried *Vivat!* In spite of everything – the weather, the peers nipping brandy and still shivering in their ermine, the sodden populace, the nonsense of these elaborate, primitive, expensive goings-on on a very small island with a bad climate and nothing much left to boast of – all the same something had happened or seemed to happen. A plumpish young woman who would rather have been at the races and clearly found the sceptre and the orb too heavy had, for a few hours, become more than herself: a spring Queen, an emblem of unreasoning hope.

Enough to send the novices gathered around Mother Martin's television set all a'flutter. Gasps and damp eyes. Even Sister Michael blew her nose with a trumpet's sound.

Ilse Lamprey thought very little of the whole thing except to wonder not for the first time that such a dull people, characterised by filthy weather and worse food, should from time to time fall into madness – collecting Empires, losing them, displaying wild courage (this very day a laconic Colonial had presented his monarch with the phallic symbol of a mountain top no one in their right mind would think of climbing); worshipping a plainish young female who was not even English, had no power to speak of, too much money, an appalling wardrobe and a passion for bagpipes.

'I think that will do,' Ilse said, 'turn it off.'

It was dusk now and for most of the day she had with surprising benevolence allowed Olga Rákosfalvi and Babakov to listen to her wireless. Babakov had nodded off several times but Olga had cried buckets into her pinny which proved nothing except that hysteria is universal and Olga had a hopelessly soft heart.

Olga sighed with satisfaction and Babakov jerked awake. Ilse was nearly ready.

'I have ordered a taxi to take you both to St Jude's meadow and return you at midnight. No! No argument. I shall stay in bed. My grey wig please, Babakov, and would you be good enough to check that Vera is in her room. Don't worry. I shall be safe enough. I have work to do. Lock my door.'

Once they had left – Babakov doubtfully, Olga gaily – Ilse Lamprey lit a cheroot, took up her board and paper and continued to write.

It was through Angela Raubal, the mother of Geli and widowed half-sister of Adolf Hitler that I first came, as occasional secretary, into the service of the leader of the NSDAP or National Socialist German Workers' Party. In those times there was nothing exceptional about taking up such a post. The duties were light. I had no politics then nor have ever had since. After a privileged childhood and the death of my parents, I found myself with an inadequate private income, no desire to marry but possessed of decent looks and competence. Those who leap to judgment should remember that history is not all monsters and heroes, victors and vanquished. There are always people like me, the passengers: those who take their place on a certain train because they do not care very much where they go or what is happening in the dining-car or the sleeping compartments or who is driving or what was that bump in the night on the line as if someone had fallen beneath the wheels. There are places we could have got off but increasingly the landscape ceases to invite, the stations are unlit and uninviting – one cannot read the names and besides it is warmer in the carriage even when the service grows unreliable and there are all kinds of terrible rumours about the destination. But by then it is too late. We have passed the last stop before the terminus and the train steams on.

Since Elenora had become a nun and there had been no response to his present of the *Epithalamion* and he cared little what became of him or where he went, Gustavus allowed himself to be carried with the crowd towards St Jude's meadow. In the Wheatmarket the darkness was broken by torch-carrying daemons with tails and tridents – a dance of death on the part of the University Dramatic Society but to Gustavus, stumbling and gasping, pressed from before and behind, these hellish figures seemed pricked out in devilry for his torment as their shadows loomed huge and he received a fearful prod from the business end of a fork. Was that Posy – the girl with wild flowers in her hair – and Janusz Grzyb? He could not tell lovers from fiends, substance from shadow, then at last there was the worst push of all and Gustavus found himself still breathing, more or less whole, on the wet grass of the meadow. He leaned panting against a tree.

'Are you all right, Professor Mowle?'

'What? Oh yes, thank you, Posy.'

'Just in time for the barge.'

'What?'

The rain had stopped, the bonfires spat sparks, jumping jacks, paused, blazed up to heaven and to watery uncertain musicke fireworks were let off, burst and fell as stars as Gloriana's barge, lit and hung with flowers, dangerous upon the flood, rounded the bend in the river, tipped, groaned and with slow majesty began to gurgle, bubble and sink.

Taking time to pull off only his shoes, Gustavus plunged, found himself in only three feet of water, waded on and in the deeper stream there was Gloriana buoyed up by her ruffle which made it also impossible to swim.

'Gloriana!'

'Gustavus!'

'Elenora!'

By midnight the barge had sunk entirely, the Mayor had had the satisfaction of observing Sir Walter Raleigh (the chairman of the University Coronation committee) helped, sodden, into the ambulance that had taken half an hour to make its way through choked streets. Even when the last of the fireworks had been spent, the bonfires dowsed by fresh showers, revellers remained, beer flowed down loyal throats and in honour of the occasion a dozen or so maidenheads were given up on the soaked grass by the river beneath the trees.

Head to head, heart to heart, arms around each other's waists, Posy and Janusz were making their way back to Radpole Road. Babakov, on Olga's arm, was leaving the Britannia where they had spent most of a very satisfactory evening, in search of their taxi. And as the last bell in this city of bells announced that the revels were officially ended, PC Bright and Inspector Fox of Paddington Green with an order for the arrest of the woman called Vera, saw from a mile away the light in the sky of the most splendid bonfire of the day as 161 Radpole Road went up in flames.

What no one saw as they assembled in the road in states of horror, shock and (in Fox's case) frustration, while the flames tenderly and then voraciously licked, teased and finally devoured the house of dreams and foreboding, was a shadow – hardly more than a ghost – that lowered itself from a ground-floor window and was gone into the night. Perhaps there was another figure, dazed, slower than the first, even less substantial, unobserved in the deep darkness beyond the bounding light of the fire, the crowd, the hoses. Perhaps not.

Two were oblivious.

Safe in his college room, Gustavus sported the oak, lit the fire, found towels and a blanket, poured brandy. Between kisses.

'Oh, Gustavus.'

Courtly, he kneeled by the couch that held his love. Not a nun, not a queen, possibly a virgin, certainly a woman.

'Was it the *Epithalamion*?'

Elenora smiled.

'Partly. But I think I'd already made up my mind. About living. It's much better than *The Faerie Queene*, don't you think?'

'Oh yes.' Gustavus adored.

' "My love is now awake out of her dream
And her fayre eyes like stars that dimmed were
With darksome cloud, now show their goodly beams." '

Elenora flung back her blanket.

'Damn poetry!' said Gustavus and leaped into bed.

Chapter Fifteen

*T*he proud winning contestant in the *Woman's Home* competition, Valerie Mowle, spent two blissful weeks at Scarborough in company with her chosen consort. They had signed the register under the name Rainbird. Every day they took a walk in the rain and watched the weather from the north come in. At night Valerie wore her new flannel nightie. She had apparently been delivered of her phantom pregnancy. As for the Detective Sergeant who would in time proudly bestow upon Valerie his name, he seemed much better after the little break in the country he did not care to discuss. Cuffy still growled at him but all he said was: 'Dogs will be dogs.' Only now and then did he strike Valerie as being not quite there – as if he were trying to remember something.

Elenora and Gustavus lived happily ever after, as did Posy and Janusz and little Grzyb, who was conceived the night of the Coronation, along with a lot of other babies. Posy never considered abortion and no one had yet thought of one-parent families, though she was probably one of the first Polish-speaking mothers to get a good degree in English language and literature. Janusz never really did learn English but they have a small, chic restaurant now in Dulwich, where the patron does the cooking. He has almost forgotten the Polish Corridor.

Inspector Fox found Ilse Lamprey's testament in a steel box by what had been her bed, in the ashes after the fire:

156

The Braun woman decided to die. She had never been of much account and is over-estimated by history. A.H. – whom some know as Gruber – was at the last moment, as one might expect, frightened to take his life. The valet SS Sturmbannführer Heinz Linge was sent to procure a body of an approximate weight and appearance, which presented no difficulty in this city of the dead. The corpse was burned and wrapped in a field-grey blanket to be discovered by the Russians. For days we had heard their guns from the Potsdamerplatz. The secretaries were given poison capsules but suicide (until this moment) has never interested me – such a dreary way to go out. Besides, as I have said, I was on the train of history and so accompanied our Führer – who overnight had become an old man and has remained so since – with others to make our way along the subway tracks below the Wilhelmsplatz. Our idea had been to proceed to the Friedrichstrasse Bahnhof and thence to cross the river Spree and slip through the Russian lines to the north. On the subway we met Babakov who, though feeble himself, helped to carry the case containing A.H.'s precious gold, which was to sustain us through the difficult times to come.

It was clear by now that A.H. was in no condition to carry out our plan and so it was that we three spent that summer hiding like so many in cellars and caves made from the debris. The last place anyone would expect to find the man we then called Gruber (from his given name) alive was Berlin. While he still had the strength he would sometimes walk about and was never once recognised. The children liked him – they called him grandfather and with Babakov helped to keep us alive. By August when 4,000 died each day I had the illness that left me bald and could not consider working in the Trümmerfrauen – the gang of women who toiled among the ruins earning their rations.

It was the winter we most feared as though the dark

157

ages were come upon us again. A.H. was out of his mind now, talking of horoscopes and a return of his cursed Reich in 1948, and the truth is we stayed with him only for the gold that made our survival possible. With it we paid for squirrel, jackdaw, raven, an egg, a few potatoes. We watched them dig our graves but then we were saved. The winter was mild, there was even a goose for dinner. A miracle, Gruber said, but I believe weather to be indifferent to human circumstance. It woke him for the moment from his raging depression and that was the last time he willingly left our shelter, to stalk, a death's-head on a pike staff, among the children at the Christmas Fair. There can never have been such a Weihnachtsmarkt: a fair organ, carousels, a tree where the statue of Wilhelm IV once stood. Babakov wept, I remember.

At the end of that winter we bought our escape with gold I had given to a Russian who made use of my body in ways I prefer not to recount. It was hard – the walk to Rostock, the concealment, the waiting for a ship, for forged passports, the voyage to Flensburg – even with the gold. Through contacts we could perhaps have reached Argentina but by then Gruber was beyond decisions and to me it seemed that the best place for a criminal to hide was among his would-be jailors. So Gottlieb of Victoria arranged our passage to England. I lost the use of my legs soon after our arrival but what use are legs if there is nowhere to go?

Now I strike the match that will end it all: Gruber, his daughter, myself. I would not wish this act to be misunderstood as judgment or courage. I have written of the daughter as the devil's spawn but it is much simpler than that. I am tired of memory, of history. There will be other monsters, other victims, other passengers. Already as I go out, bearing with me Gruber and his daughter, I see the warmly lit windows, the travellers taking their seats, the train approaching, gathering speed . . .

The evidence was filed, suppressed, forgotten. Babakov remembered Ilse Lamprey sometimes and Olga comforted him. With the cunning of cats, Shadow escaped the fire, as did Aeneas.

The television set Father Clement had hired for the Little Flowers of St Anne was carried away. Mother Martin saw it go with only a little regret for *I Love Lucy*. The novices settled down again and their clear song rose along with the mindless doves. Among them in chapel was the girl who had arrived wearing a grey cloak at the gatehouse in the dark and the rain, asking for sanctuary. She had forgotten who she was and perhaps that was the reason that hers was of all faces, the purest by far. When later, at her own request, she joined the Mission of the Little Flowers of St Anne in Vietnam, formerly known as French Indo-China, she was greatly missed.